ASSESSMENT OF HEAVY METAL CONTAMINATION IN THE MARINE ENVIRONMENT OF THE ARABIAN GULF

ENVIRONMENTAL HEALTH - PHYSICAL, CHEMICAL AND BIOLOGICAL FACTORS

MARINE BIOLOGY

ENVIRONMENTAL HEALTH -
PHYSICAL, CHEMICAL AND BIOLOGICAL FACTORS

ASSESSMENT OF HEAVY METAL CONTAMINATION IN THE MARINE ENVIRONMENT OF THE ARABIAN GULF

HUMOOD ABDULLA NASER

New York

For permission to use material from this book please contact us:
Telephone 631-231-7269; Fax 631-231-8175
Web Site: http://www.novapublishers.com

NOTICE TO THE READER

The Publisher has taken reasonable care in the preparation of this book, but makes no expressed or implied warranty of any kind and assumes no responsibility for any errors or omissions. No liability is assumed for incidental or consequential damages in connection with or arising out of information contained in this book. The Publisher shall not be liable for any special, consequential, or exemplary damages resulting, in whole or in part, from the readers' use of, or reliance upon, this material. Any parts of this book based on government reports are so indicated and copyright is claimed for those parts to the extent applicable to compilations of such works.

Independent verification should be sought for any data, advice or recommendations contained in this book. In addition, no responsibility is assumed by the publisher for any injury and/or damage to persons or property arising from any methods, products, instructions, ideas or otherwise contained in this publication.

This publication is designed to provide accurate and authoritative information with regard to the subject matter covered herein. It is sold with the clear understanding that the Publisher is not engaged in rendering legal or any other professional services. If legal or any other expert assistance is required, the services of a competent person should be sought. FROM A DECLARATION OF PARTICIPANTS JOINTLY ADOPTED BY A COMMITTEE OF THE AMERICAN BAR ASSOCIATION AND A COMMITTEE OF PUBLISHERS.

Additional color graphics may be available in the e-book version of this book.

Library of Congress Cataloging-in-Publication Data
Naser, Humood Abdulla.
  Assessment of heavy metal contamination in the marine environment of the Arabian Gulf / Humood Abdulla Naser.
      pages cm
  Includes bibliographical references and index.
   ISBN: 978-1-62417-619-7 (soft cover)
  1. Marine pollution--Persian Gulf. 2. Heavy metals--Environmental aspects--Persian Gulf. 3. Persian Gulf--Environmental conditions. I. Title.
   GC1451.N36 2013
   363.738'49--dc23
                          2012048209

Published by Nova Science Publishers, Inc. † New York

This Book Is Dedicated to My Family

CONTENTS

PREFACE

The Arabian Gulf is characterized by physical, chemical and biological uniqueness. It is considered the hottest water body in the world. Marine organisms and ecosystems in the Arabian Gulf are unique as they thrive despite extreme environmental conditions such as marked fluctuations in sea temperatures and elevated levels of salinity.

Heavy metals are serious threats to ecosystems and human health due to their toxicity, persistence and bioaccumulation characteristics. The coasts of the Arabian Gulf are witnessing rapid industrialization and urbanization that contribute to heavy metal loads in the coastal and marine habitats. Continuous inputs of heavy metals from different anthropogenic sources in the Arabian Gulf could be critical for both the naturally stressed marine ecosystems and humans who rely on marine resources for food, recreation and industry.

This book identifies valued ecosystem components in the Arabian Gulf, characterizes sources of anthropogenic impacts, assesses the heavy metal contamination in a variety of living organisms, seawaters and sediments, and suggests measures for the environmental management of heavy metal pollution in the Arabian Gulf.

This book should be useful for professionals in the fields of ecological and environmental studies, coastal and marine monitoring and management. The book can serve as an academic textbook in environmental pollution discipline. It is also intended to inform decision-makers and environmental managers as well as members of the public with a general interest in the environment of the Arabian Gulf.

ABBREVIATIONS

Al	Aluminum
As	Arsenic
Ba	Barium
Be	Beryllium
Cd	Cadmium
Cr	Chromium
Co	Cobalt
Cu	Copper
Fe	Iron
Hg	Mercury
Pb	Lead
Mn	Manganese
Mo	Molybdenum
Ni	Nickel
Sb	Antimony
Se	Selenium
Tl	Thallium
V	Vanadium
Zn	Zinc

Chapter 1

GENERAL INTRODUCTION

WHY ARE HEAVY METALS A MAJOR CONCERN?

Heavy metals are naturally found in air, waters, sediments and rocks. They can be introduced to the marine environments through atmospheric deposition, leaching of soils, and erosion (Kennish, 2001). Anthropogenic activities, particularly industries such as metal plating, mining, fertilizer industries, batteries and pesticides, are continuously increasing the amount of heavy metals in the marine environments.

Globally, wastewaters containing high levels of heavy metals are directly or indirectly discharged into the marine environments, especially in developing countries (Fu and Wang, 2011).

According to DeForest et al. (2007) heavy metals are considered a serious threat to human health, living organisms and natural ecosystems because of their toxicity, persistence and bioaccumulation characteristics. Generally, substances which are toxic pose a greater hazard when they are both persistent and bioaccumulative. Many heavy metal ions are known to be toxic or carcinogenic to humans (Fu and Wang, 2011). Additionally, heavy metals can directly affect marine organisms by reducing species diversity and abundance, and indirectly through the accumulation of metals in living organisms and food chains, which eventually poses threats to humans. Heavy metals are persistent in the marine environment due to interactions between water, sediment and atmosphere (DeForest et al., 2007). They are considered among the most persistent environmental pollutants in seawaters and biota, and their occurrence in sediments indicates the presence of natural or anthropogenic sources (Rahman and Ishiga, 2012).

THE NEED TO MONITOR HEAVY METALS IN MARINE ENVIRONMENTS

Monitoring is a scientific technique for assessing the environment, including human exposure to natural and synthetic chemicals, and heavy metals. Monitoring is conducted by sampling and analysis of an individual organism's tissues and fluids as well as the environmental matrix, such as water and sediment, to reveal the heavy metal pollution status in the marine environments (Zhou et al., 2008).

Many marine organisms, including molluscs (Perez-Lopez et al., 2003), crustaceans (Blackmore et al., 1998; Farkas et al., 2003; Guerra-Garcia et al., 2010), fish (Al-Saleh and Shinwari, 2002), algae (Davis et al., 2003; Conti and Cecchetti, 2003), barnacles (Reis et al., 2012), seagrass (Thangaradjou et al., 2010, 2012) and coral reefs (Ali et al., 2011), are utilized as bio-monitors for heavy metal contamination in marine environments.

Marine sediments are the final destination of substances produced in surface waters or introduced into the sea through natural and anthropogenic processes (Valdes, 2012). Sediments can accumulate various pollutants and are widely used for the environmental monitoring of human impact. Sediments act as a sink for heavy metals and other pollutants in coastal and marine environments (Berg et al., 2001). Heavy metal concentrations in seawaters are generally correlated with those in marine organisms and sediments (Perez-Lopez et al., 2003). Therefore, heavy metal levels in seawater are regularly monitored to detect environmental pollution in coastal and marine environments worldwide (Juma and Al-Madany, 2008).

WHAT IS UNIQUE ABOUT THE ARABIAN GULF?

The Arabian Gulf (Figure 1.1) is a semi-enclosed sea (total area of around 240,000 km^2) situated in the subtropical zone and characterized by marked fluctuations in sea temperatures and high salinities. Summer water temperatures can exceed 36°C and winter values may fall below 15°C (Riegl and Purkis, 2012). Salinity can exceed 43 psu in the southern part of the Arabian Gulf and could reach 70-80 psu in areas with restricted flow such as tidal pools and lagoons due to high evaporation rates. The Arabian Gulf is a relatively shallow basin with an average depth of 35m (Sheppard et al., 2010).

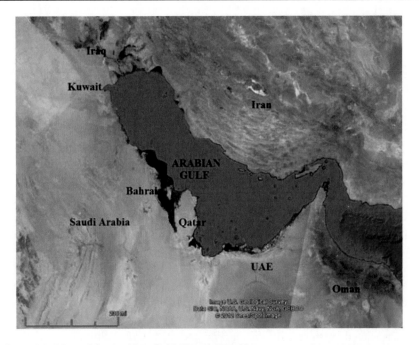

Figure 1.1. Map of the Arabian Gulf (Google Earth).

Flora and fauna species in the Arabian Gulf inhabit one of the harshest marine environments due to natural stressors represented by higher levels of salinity and temperature, and reduced levels of pH (Uddin et al., 2012). Native marine organisms of the Arabian Gulf are living close to the limits of their environmental tolerance (Price et al., 1993).

Despite these harsh environmental conditions, the Arabian Gulf supports a range of coastal and marine habitats such as mangrove swamps, seagrass beds, coral reefs, and mud and sand flats (Naser, 2011a). These habitats provide feeding and nursery grounds for a variety of marine organisms, including a number of valuable commercial species (Carpenter et al. 1997).

Anthropogenically, the Arabian Gulf is considered among the highest impacted regions in the world (Halpern et al., 2008). Coastal development associated with intensive dredging and reclamation is increasingly contributing to the degradation of marine ecosystems (Naser, 2011b).

Sources of heavy metal inputs into marine environment of the Arabian Gulf include industrial waste, brine waste waters, ports and refiners, oil spills, domestic sewage, and pollution from other land-based activities (Naser, 2011a).

WHY MONITOR HEAVY METALS IN THE ARABIAN GULF?

People of the Arabian Gulf are related economically and socially to the sea. The waters of the Arabian Gulf are rich in various species of fish, which are a major source of food for people in the Arabian Gulf. Therefore, it is important to assess and monitor the levels of heavy metals in marine organisms because of nutritional safety conditions.

Coastal and marine environments in the Arabian Gulf contribute substantially to the sectors of fishery, trade, shipping, tourism, electricity production, water desalination and the utilization of coastal areas by industry. Most of the fresh water needs in the Arabian Gulf countries are obtained from seawater through the various processes of desalination (Hashim and Hajjaj, 2005). Therefore, monitoring marine pollution and the detection of point source pollutant is crucial for the desalination industry.

The flushing time of seawater has been estimated to be in the range of 3–5 years, indicating that pollutants such as heavy metals are likely to reside in the Arabian Gulf for a considerable time. Additionally, the Arabian Gulf countries are witnessing rapid industrialization and urbanization developments that may be associated with environmental degradation and pollution. Additional anthropogenic inputs of heavy metals to the naturally stressed marine environment of the Arabian Gulf might be critical not only to vulnerable and fragile ecosystems, but also to human health.

AIMS AND SCOPE OF THE BOOK

This book aims to 1) identify valued ecosystem components and their ecological goods and services that could be affected by heavy metal pollution in the Arabian Gulf, 2) characterize existing anthropogenic impacts contributing to heavy metal loads in coastal and marine environments of the Arabian Gulf, 3) review the existing published information on heavy metal levels in the various components of the marine ecosystems in the Arabian Gulf, 4) investigate the spatial distribution of heavy metals in a heavily industrialized coastal zone in Bahrain, and 5) suggest measures that may contribute to the management of heavy metals in the coastal and marine environments in the Arabian Gulf.

This book could be very important as baseline data for future monitoring programmes in the Arabian Gulf. Additionally, this may help in developing and implementing heavy metal management plans in the marine environment of the Arabian Gulf.

This book constitutes twelve chapters. Chapter 2 provides a brief background to valued marine ecosystems in the Arabian Gulf, including seagrass beds, coral reefs, mangroves and mudflats. Chapter 3 identifies the main anthropogenic sources of heavy metals in the Arabian Gulf, including sediment mobilization due to dredging and reclamation activities, effluents from sewage treatment plants, industrial facilities, desalination plants and oil spills. Chapter 4 explores the role of marine algae as bioindicators for heavy metal pollution, and summarizes the levels of heavy metals in algal species from the Arabian Gulf. Chapter 5 outlines the advantages of using molluscs as bioindicators for environmental pollution, and reviews the levels of heavy metals in molluscs from the Arabian Gulf. Chapter 6 deals with the heavy metal contents in fish bodies. Chapter 7 provides a brief summary of concentrations of heavy metals in seawater samples analyzed by some studies. Chapter 8 outlines the role of sediments as the main sink for heavy metal contaminants, and reviews levels of heavy metals in contaminated sediments. Chapter 9 explores the utilization of macrobenthic community structure as a tool to detect and evaluate heavy metal pollution in the Arabian Gulf. Chapter 10 provides a detailed case study for monitoring heavy metals in marine sediments influenced by anthropogenic activities. This study involves characterizing anthropogenic sources of heavy metals in Bahrain, illustrating spatial sampling designed to detect the gradient of heavy metal pollution, and comparing metal concentrations with relevant standards and guidelines. Chapter 11 suggests measures that my help in controlling and preventing heavy metal pollution in the Arabian Gulf, including environmental impact assessment, national and regional environmental laws dealing with heavy metal pollution, and scientific research and technology. Chapter 12 summarizes the main findings of the book and suggests recommendations that may contribute to heavy metal management in the Arabian Gulf.

Chapter 2

VALUED ECOSYSTEM COMPONENTS IN THE ARABIAN GULF

WHAT ARE VALUED ECOSYSTEM COMPONENTS?

Advancing environmental management and monitoring of pollution caused by varieties of pollutants, including heavy metals, requires identifying key elements of impacted environment. Aspects of the environment that are considered ecologically important are called Valued Ecosystem Components (VECs) (Treweek 1999). Coastal and marine environments in the Arabian Gulf support important VECs such as seagrass and algal beds, mangroves, intertidal mudflats and coral reefs. These ecosystems contribute significantly to the productivity of marine resources in the Arabian Gulf (Khan et al., 2002).

SEAGRASS BEDS

As a result of the relative shallowness of the Arabian Gulf, most of its floor is within the photic zone. Hence, a wide range of the bottom is covered with seagrass beds (Figure 2.1). Seagrass beds are highly productive ecosystems that provide important ecological functions and economic services (Sheppard et al., 1992; Duarte, 2002; Duffy, 2006). Ecologically, seagrass ecosystems provide food sources and function as feeding grounds for threatened species such as turtles and dugongs (Price et al., 1993; Preen, 2004; Abdulqader and Miller, 2012; Preen et al., 2012). They can also improve water quality by stabilizing loose sediment and by filtering some pollutants out of the water (Duffy, 2006). Economically, they serve as important nursery grounds for penaeid shrimps, pearl oysters and other organisms of importance to the Arabian Gulf's commercial fisheries (Abdulqader, 1999; Erftemeijer and Shuail, 2012).

Seagrass beds are extensively distributed along the shores of the countries surrounding the Arabian Gulf. Around 7 000 km^2 of seagrass habitat have been mapped in the Arabian Gulf to date (Erftemeijer and Shuail, 2012). Three species of seagrass occur in the Arabian Gulf; namely, *Halodule uninervis*, *Halophila stipulacea* and *Halophila ovalis* (Phillips, 2003).

However, these ecosystems are intensively subjected to human disturbance either by direct physical damage or by deterioration of the water quality resulting from increasing levels of pollution. Several land-based activities are discharging waste waters associated with elevated levels of heavy metals. These activities potentially pose threats to seagrass ecosystems in the Arabian Gulf (Al-Wedaei et al., 2011).

Heavy metals can be incorporated into seagrass tissues from either water column or sediment. Toxic concentrations of heavy metals in seagrass tissues can inhibit metabolic activity and interfere with vital biochemical pathways such as photosynthesis (Rappe, 2010).

Figure 2.1. Seagrass habitats are recognized as a critical marine resource in the Arabian Gulf.

Therefore, contamination with heavy metals may be one of the significant factors controlling the growth of seagrasses (Nobi et al., 2010). Seagrass habitats support greater macro-fauna species diversity, abundance and biomass than adjacent unvegetated habitats (Coles and McCain, 1990, Al-Khayat, 2007).

Decreased levels in species richness of seagrass fauna have been reported in contaminated seagrass beds (Rappe, 2010). Additionally, as detritus in seagrass beds provide an indirect source of food for many marine organisms, heavy metals may enter the food chain of the marine environment.

CORAL REEFS

Coral reefs are characterized by both biological diversity and high levels of productivity. These ecosystems provide a variety of ecological services such as renewable sources of seafood, maintenance of genetic, biological and habitat diversity, recreational values, and economic benefits such as utilizing destructive reefs for creating land (Moberg and Folke, 1999). The high diversity of coral reefs provides a wide range of habitats for other reef species and fish. Coral reefs in the Arabian Gulf have traditionally been important habitats for fisheries.

Because corals in the Arabian Gulf are exposed to extremes in temperature, salinity and other physical factors, their development is patchy. However, despite these harsh environmental conditions, corals in the Arabian Gulf exhibit remarkable resilience and vitality (Riegl and Purkis, 2012).

Additionally, coral reefs in the Arabian Gulf have been severely affected by bleaching events as well as human impacts such as sediment runoff from dredging and reclamation activities and pollution, including heavy metals, from different land-based sources.

Corals are sensitive to the physical and chemical changes in the marine environment. According to Ali et al., (2011) the responses of corals to elevated levels of heavy metals include physiological stress, inhibition of coral fertilization and reduced reproductive success, decreased settlement and survival of coral larvae, changes in the population and growth of the endosymbiotic algae (zooxanthellae), changes in the rate of photosynthesis, and increased coral bleaching and mortality.

Anthropogenically introduced heavy metals in nearshore waters not only pose threats to the health of corals, but also pose health risks to humans who rely on fish and other marine resources from coral reefs.

MANGROVE SWAMPS

Mangrove habitats are ecologically important coastal ecosystems that provide food, shelter and nursery areas for a variety of terrestrial and marine fauna (Hogarth, 1999; Saenger, 2002).

Mangrove habitats of the Arabian Gulf support a variety of important species of fish, shrimps, turtles and birds, and significantly contribute to the coastal productivity (Barth and Khan, 2008).

Mangroves, represented by the single species *Avicennia marina*, are largely distributed along the southern shores of the Arabian Gulf (Figure 2.2). However, these ecosystems are subjected to increasing pressures from coastal development and pollution (Sheppard et al., 2010).

Mangrove ecosystems are close to urban development areas. They are impacted by industrial and sewage effluents that contain elevated levels of heavy metals. For instance, the remaining stands of mangroves in Bahrain (0.31 km^2) receive around 160,000 m^3 of treated and partially treated sewage effluents from the main treatment plant on a daily basis (Naser, 2011a).

Figure 2.2. Mangrove swamps, *Avicennia marina*, are important coastal ecosystems in the Arabian Gulf.

The anaerobic and reduced characteristics of mangrove sediments allow the retention of water-borne heavy metals and the subsequent metal mobilization and bioavailability (Shriadah, 1999; Defew, et al., 2005). Bayen (2012) provides a recent review on bioavailability and the toxic effects of heavy metals in mangrove ecosystems.

MUDFLATS

Muddy substrata are the most widespread habitats, which extend from intertidal salt marshes to the maximum depth in the Arabian Gulf (Sheppard et al., 2010). Given that more than 97% of the bottom substrate of the Arabian Gulf is dominated by sand and mud (Al-Ghadban, 2002), macrobenthos form the largest and most diverse marine ecosystem. Tidal mudflats and coastal wetlands in the Arabian Gulf support high levels of benthos diversity. They also contribute significantly to fisheries' productivity and provide feeding and roosting grounds for shorebird populations (Figure 2.3) (Abdulqader, 1999; Al-Sayed et al., 2008).

Figure 2.3. Tidal muddy flats provide important feeding grounds for wader birds in the Arabian Gulf.

Figure 2.4. Algal mats in tidal mudflats contribute to primary productivity of coastal ecosystems in the Arabian Gulf.

Additionally, mudflats support dense algal mats, which play important roles in grazing food chains (Figure 2.4).

The rapid reclamation activities along the coastline of the Arabian Gulf have resulted in the loss of many prime mudflat habitats. Furthermore, these habitats are influenced by industrial and sewage effluents, and discharges from desalination plants, which are characterized by high inputs of heavy metals (Naser, 2011a).

Macrobenthic assemblages in soft-sediments may respond to heavy metal pollution by changes in their community structures represented by alterations in abundance, biomass and species diversity (Naser, 2010a).

Chapter 3

ANTHROPOGENIC SOURCES OF HEAVY METALS IN THE ARABIAN GULF

WHY IS IT NECESSARY TO IDENTIFY SOURCES OF CONTAMINATION?

In the past few decades, Arabian Gulf countries have witnessed major economic, social and industrial developments.

The coastlines of the Arabian Gulf have been extensively developed and modified to accommodate mega-projects including artificial islands, waterfront cities, ports and marinas. These developments are typically accompanied by several anthropogenic stressors that contribute to environmental degradation, which warrant the classification of the Arabian Gulf among the highest anthropogenically impacted regions in the world (Halpern et al., 2008).

Such impacts include dredging and reclamation, industrial and sewage effluents, hypersaline water discharges from desalination plants, and oil pollution (Sheppard et al., 2010).

All of these anthropogenic activities are mobilizing and discharging elevated levels of heavy metals into the marine environment of the Arabian Gulf.

Identifying origins and sources of contamination can aid in designing and implementing preventative and control measures of heavy metals. This chapter therefore explores the main anthropogenic sources of pollution that contribute to the heavy metals load in the coastal and marine environments of the Arabian Gulf.

RECLAMATION AND DREDGING

The coasts of the Arabian Gulf are undergoing rapid construction activities that are often associated with intensive dredging and reclamation (Price and Sheppard, 1991). Coastal and marine environments in the Arabian Gulf are the prime target for most of the major housing, recreational and economic developments (Naser et al., 2008). Coastal developments along the Arabian Gulf have accelerated at an unprecedented rate in the past decade (Khan, 2007). It is currently estimated that more than 40% of the coasts of the Arabian Gulf have been developed (Hamza and Munawar, 2009). For example, reclamation activities in Bahrain resulted in the addition of around 95 km^2 representing an increase of 12% of the total land area (Figures 3.1 and 3.2). It is likely that reclamation will accelerate in the coming decades in order to secure land for large-scale projects as populations in the Arabian Gulf countries continue to grow. For instance, the Bahrain National Land Use Strategy 2030 recognizes reclamation as the major option for securing the future needs for land, indicating that the coastal environment in Bahrain will continue to be the major focus for developmental projects in the future (Naser, 2011b).

Figure 3.1. Coastal reclamation is regularly carried out in Bahrain to meet the demands of rapid coastal developments. Heavy metals can be mobilized into coastal and marine environments due to intensive reclamation activities.

During the reclamation and dredging processes, sand and mud, characterized by lower levels of biodiversity and abundance, are extracted from designated borrow areas then dumped into coastal and subtidal areas, characterized by high levels of biodiversity and productivity (Naser, 2010a).

Dredging and reclamation processes are typically associated with short- and long-term biological, physical and chemical impacts. These activities involve the direct removal of macrobenthos and result in physically smothering the coastal and subtidal habitats and deoxygenating the underlining sediments (Newell et al., 1998; Allan et al., 2008).

These physical and chemical alternations may reduce the biodiversity, richness, abundance and biomass of marine organisms (Smith and Rule, 2001). Additionally, elevated levels of heavy metals are mobilized during dredging and reclamation activities (Guerra et al., 2009; Hedge et al., 2009). These contaminants may enter important food web components, including fish and shellfish, and ultimately pose threats to human health.

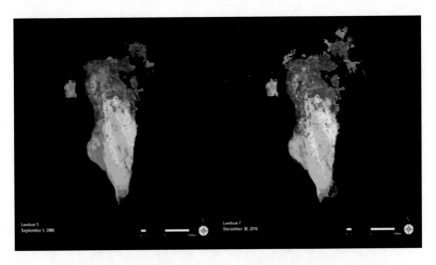

Figure 3.2. A historical map obtained from U.S. Geological Survey (www.usgs.gov) showing the rapid changes in the coastlines of Bahrain between 2000 and 2010.

SEWAGE DISCHARGES

Sewage discharges are a major source of coastal pollution in the Arabian Gulf countries (Figure 3.3). Despite high standards of sewage treatment throughout the Arabian Gulf countries (Sheppard et al. 2010), large quantities of domestic effluents are discharged to coastal and marine environments. These effluents are characterized by high-suspended solids and a high load of nutrients such as ammonia, nitrates and phosphates (Naser, 2011a). Sewage effluents are generally accompanied by biological and chemical pollutants, including heavy metals (Al-Muzaini et al., 1999; Shatti and Abdullah, 1999) that may cause degradation in the receiving coastal and marine environments, and subsequently affect the quality of human food and health (Singh et al., 2004).

INDUSTRIAL EFFLUENTS

The Arabian Gulf countries have witnessed a rapid industrial growth, mainly in the sectors of oil refining and petrochemical industries (figures 3.4 and 3.5).

Figure 3.3. Sewage effluents are a major source of heavy metal loads in the coastal and marine environments of the Arabian Gulf.

Figure 3.4. Petrochemical industries along the coastlines of the Arabian Gulf are discharging effluents that contain high levels of heavy metals.

Figure 3.5. Oil refineries in the Arabian Gulf discharge effluents that contain elevated levels of hydrocarbons and heavy metals.

These major industries are discharging wastewater containing a variety of chemicals, including heavy metals, hydrocarbon compounds and nutrients

(Sale et al., 2010). Petroleum refinery wastewaters are composed of different chemicals, which include oil and greases, phenols, sulphides, ammonia, suspended solids, and heavy metals like chromium, iron, nickel, copper, molybdenum, selenium, vanadium and zinc (Wake, 2005).

Coastal and marine environments receiving intensive industrial effluents along the coastline of the Arabian Gulf are recognized as hotspots for high concentrations of heavy metals (De Mora et al., 2004) and hydrocarbons (De Mora et al., 2010). In Bahrain, for example, around 1, 793, 294 m^3 day^{-1} of industrial effluents characterized by high inputs of heavy metals and hydrocarbons are discharged into the shallow subtidal areas off the eastern coastline (Naser, 2011a).

DESALINATION PLANTS

The Arabian Gulf countries are witnessing rapid industrial development and population growth, which increase the need for fresh water (Smith et al., 2007).

Due to the low precipitation and high aridity in the Arabian Gulf countries, most of the fresh water needs are being satisfied by seawater through the various processes of desalination (Figure 3.6), including multi-stage flash, and seawater/brackish reverse osmosis (Hashim and Hajjaj, 2005). For instance, approximately 90% of the potable water need in Kuwait is obtained from desalinated water.

Globally, it is estimated that the amount of desalinated water in the Arabian Gulf countries accounts for more than 60% of the world's total production (Lattemann and Hopner, 2008a). Large quantities of rejected water from desalination plants are being discharged on a daily basis to coastal and subtidal areas in the Arabian Gulf. For example, the shallow coastal and marine environments in Bahrain receive around 8 000 m^3 day^{-1} of waste water from four major desalination plants (Naser, 2010a). Hypersaline water discharges associated with chemical products, including heavy metals from desalination plants, are increasingly becoming a serious threat to coastal and marine ecosystems in the Arabian Gulf (Areiqat and Mohamed, 2005). Heavy metals are considered a by-product of the desalination processes due to corrosion (Lattemann and Hopner, 2008b).

Elevated levels of heavy metals have been reported in close proximity to several desalination plants along the coastline of the Arabian Gulf (Sadiq, 2002; Naser, 2010b, 2012a).

Figure 3.6. Desalination plants are a major source of heavy metal inputs to the coastal and marine environments in the Arabian Gulf.

OIL POLLUTION

The Arabian Gulf is considered the largest reserve of oil in the world, with more than 25 000 tankers navigating through the Strait of Hormuz each year (Literathy et al., 2002). Oil exploration, production and transport have been major contributors to pollution in the Arabian Gulf. Indeed, coastal and marine environments in the Arabian Gulf are under permanent threat from oil-related pollution (MEMAC, 2003). Sources of oil spills in the Arabian Gulf include offshore oil wells, underwater pipelines, oil tanker incidents, oil terminals, loading and handling operations, weathered oil and tar balls, illegal dumping of ballast water and military activities (Sale et al., 2010). The Arabian Gulf was the scene for one of the most notorious oil spill incidents in the world. During the 1991 Gulf War, an estimated 10.8 million barrels of oil were spilled in the Arabian Gulf waters (Massoud et al., 1998). Several scientific reports reported high levels of environmental pollution in the marine environment of the Arabian Gulf after this major oil spill, including elevated levels of heavy metals (Al-Arfaj and Alam 1993). Several studies investigating the long-term environmental impacts of this oil spill on the terrestrial and marine environments were conducted (Price and Robinson, 1993; Massoud et al., 1998; Jones et al., 1998; Joydas et al,. 2012). On the other hand, smaller scale incidents of oil spill are more frequent in the Arabian Gulf than in other parts of the world. These incidents include leakages in pipelines, over-flooding of containers, weathered oil and tar balls, and incidents during the loading of tankers in the terminals.

Chapter 4

HEAVY METAL LEVELS IN ALGAL SPECIES FROM THE ARABIAN GULF

MARINE ALGAE AS BIOINDICATORS FOR HEAVY METAL POLLUTION

Marine algae are photosynthetic organisms that contribute to the overall productivity of marine ecosystems (Moberg and Ronnback 2003). Diversity and abundance of marine algae can directly reflect the quality of seawater (Campanella et al., 2000).

Due to their wide abundance and distribution along the worldwide seashores, marine algae are increasingly used as bioindicators to monitor heavy metal contamination (Torres et al., 2008). Exposure of marine algae to heavy metal pollution can interfere with normal metabolism and biological functions, inhibit the photosynthesis process, and may subsequently lead to the degradation of these algae (Zhou et al., 2008). Accumulated heavy metal pollutants in the algal tissues may enter the food chain and pose direct threats to marine organisms and human health due to the process of biomagnification (Al-Homaidan, 2007).

Therefore, characterizing species diversity and abundance, and analyzing biological responses and residue contents of algae can determine the level of water pollution due to heavy metal contaminants (Lavoie et al., 2004; Zhou et al., 2008).

HEAVY METAL LEVELS IN ALGAL SPECIES
FROM THE ARABIAN GULF

The Arabian Gulf supports a variety of marine algal species belonging to 207 taxa (Basson, 1992). A recent study conducted by Abdel-Kareem (2009) reported 13 new records for algal species in the Arabian Gulf. Algal species significantly contribute to the primary productivity in the Arabian Gulf (Al-Yamani et al., 2006).

Algal species have been used as bioindicators of heavy metal pollution along the coasts of the Arabian Gulf, including Qatar, Kuwait, Bahrain and Saudi Arabia (Kureishey, 1991; El-Sayed and Dorgham 1994; Kureishey et al., 1995; Buo-Olayan and Subrahmanyam, 1996; Mohamed, 2002; Al-Homaidan, 2006, 2007).

Kureishey (1991) measured the levels of Hg, Cd, Pb, Cu, Zn, Ni, Co, and Fe in some species of marine macroalgae around the Qatari coast. Although the eastern coastline of Qatar is occupied by major industries such as petrochemical, steel, and fertilizers along with desalination and power plants, levels of heavy metals in macroalgae collected from the east coast were comparable with those sampled from the north and west stations. The study concluded that the values of heavy metals measured in Qatari macroalgae were on the lower side of the values reported by other studies in some oceanic areas and estuaries.

Similar findings were reported by El-Sayed and Dorgham (1994). This study measured the levels of Fe, Mn, Zn, Cu, Ni, Cr, Cd and Hg in ten species of macroalgae collected from the Qatari coasts. The concentrations of measured metals were generally comparable with the pervious study conducted by Kureishey (1991), suggesting a non-polluted environment. However, the study reported high levels of Fe and Cd.

A trend of increasing heavy metal concentrations in algal species was detected in several subsequent studies, indicating evidence of heavy metal contamination from anthropogenic sources. The concentrations of Hg, Cd, Pb, Cu, Co and Ni were measured in algae species (*Sargassum binderi*, *Sargassum boyeanum* and *Hormophysa triquetra*) along the eastern coast of Saudi Arabia and the Qatari shores (Kureishey et al., 1995). This study investigated the potential use of marine algae as bioindicators of pollution in the Arabian Gulf.

A marked increase in the levels of measured heavy metals was detected in macroalgae collected from an area influenced by the outfalls from the industrialized city of Jubail in Saudi Arabia. A similar trend of increasing levels of heavy metals was observed around an industrial site near the capital city of Doha in Qatar compared with non-industrial and non-urban areas. Additionally, slightly higher values of heavy metals were observed in two areas influenced by oil exploration activities in Qatar. Kureishey et al. (1995) indicated a strong bioaccumulation potential for heavy metals in the investigated algal species and concluded that these species could be used as effective bioindicators for pollution levels in the Arabian Gulf.

Buo-Olayan and Subrahmanyam (1996) analyzed seven heavy metals, Cu, Fe, Mn, Ni, Pb, V and Zn, in 26 algal species collected from different areas along the Kuwaiti coastline. Higher levels of heavy metals were found in algae collected from two areas receiving high quantities of domestic sewage and industrial waste. This study indicated that filamentous algae generally showed the ability to concentrate greater amounts of heavy metals than foliaceous algae. The study also revealed that the concentrations of heavy metals in marine algae of the Kuwaiti coastline were on the high side compared to the earlier study conducted by Kureishey (1991) on the Qatari coast. However, the study attributed the high concentrations of heavy metals to natural environmental factors such as pH, temperature, salinity, nutrients in seawater, water movement and the recycling of the mineral elements after decomposition of organisms in the seawater.

The heavy metals Zn, Cu, Cd, Ni, Pb and Cr were determined in the marine algal species *Hormophysa triquetra* collected from three areas along the coastline of Bahrain (Mohamed, 2002). Generally, the results of this study showed variations in the levels of heavy metals between the three selected sites. The concentrations of Cd, Pb, Cu and Ni in the algal species *Hormophysa triquetra* measured by Mohamed (2002) in Bahrain were generally higher than equivalent metals in the same species collected from the Saudi and the Qatari coasts and reported by Kureishey et al. (1995).

Al-Homaidan (2006) measured the concentrations of Cd, Cu, Fe, Pb and Zn in four brown algae (*Padina gymnospora*, *Cystoseira myrica*, *Hormophysa triquetra* and *Sargassum angustifolium*) collected from two areas along the Saudi coast of the Arabian Gulf. The study found relatively normal concentrations for Cd, Cu, and Zn in brown algae compared with relevant studies conducted in coastal areas of the Canary Islands, the UK and Italy. However, the study reported an elevated concentration of Fe that ranged between 161 and 1,466 $\mu g\ g^{-1}$ dry weight. Normal ranges of Fe concentration in *Fucus vesiculosus* from coastal areas in the northeast of England varied between 100-250 $\mu g\ g^{-1}$ as reported by Giusti (2001). Values of >1,000 $\mu g\ g^{-1}$ were reported in the brown alga *Cystoseira barbata* collected from a polluted area on the Turkish Coast of the Black Sea (Topcuoglu et al., 2003). Additionally, Al-Homaidan (2006) detected very high concentrations of Pb along the Saudi coast of the Arabian Gulf that ranged between 8.84 and 18.60 $\mu g\ g^{-1}$.

According to Lozano et al. (2003), a concentration of Pb in algal species that exceeds 10 $\mu g\ g^{-1}$ is usually associated with contaminated areas. The Pb concentrations measured by Homaidan (2006) were generally higher than those previously reported from the same area by Kureishy et al. (1995). Homaidan (2006) attributed this increase in concentration to a gradual increase in the concentration of Pb and other contaminants over a period of ten years separating the two studies.

More recently, Homaidan (2007) measured the concentrations of Cu, Zn, Fe, Cd, Pb and Ni in three species of green algae (*Chaetomorpha aerea*, *Enteromorpha clathrata* and *Ulva lactuca*) collected from three areas along the coastline of the Saudi coast of the Arabian Gulf. The mean concentrations of metals in the examined algae were 8.41-48.52, 34.16-68.18, 812-2335, 13.90-30.50 and 25.51-44.51 $\mu g\ g^{-1}$ dry weight for Cu, Zn, Fe, Pb and Ni, respectively. Concentrations of measured heavy metals, apart from Cd, were similar to those reported in polluted coastal areas in Greece, New Zealand and Hong Kong. The study indicated a high degree of pollution in the three investigated sites, and attributed the elevated levels of heavy metals to the rapid industrialization and urbanization as well as oil spillages in the Arabian Gulf.

HEAVY METAL LEVELS IN PHYTOPLANKTON SPECIES

Phytoplankton organisms are sensitive to the presence of a wide range of pollutants, including heavy metals. Therefore, the diversity and abundance of phytoplankton can be used as indicators of water quality (Javed, 2006).

Al-Tisan and Chandy (1995) investigated the distribution of heavy metals in phytoplankton at nineteen offshore stations in the Arabian Gulf. This study was conducted during the second cruise of Umitaka Maru in December 1993. The study indicated that the distribution of heavy metals in phytoplankton varied widely in the marine environment of the Arabian Gulf. It also concluded that most of the investigated areas were free from metal contamination apart from three stations where elevated levels of Hg, As, Se, and Cd were detected.

Heavy metal concentrations in phytoplankton (diatoms and dinoflagellates) were determined in seven locations along the Kuwaiti coast (Bu-Olayan et al., 2001). The study detected high levels of heavy metals Zn, Cu, Ni, and Pb with mean concentrations of 60.00, 55.57, 40.58, and 46.52 μgg^{-1}, respectively in Kuwait Bay. The study attributed these elevated levels of heavy metals to the upwelling of water current leading to the bay, increased inputs of sewage, domestic and industrial effluents, and increased human activity in that region.

The above studies provide evidence that anthropogenic activities in the Arabian Gulf are increasingly contributing to heavy metal contamination in the coastal and marine ecosystems. High levels of heavy metal concentrations are progressively recorded in algal species influenced by sources of anthropogenic pollution.

Chapter 5

HEAVY METAL LEVELS IN MOLLUSCS FROM THE ARABIAN GULF

MOLLUSCS AS BIOINDICATORS FOR HEAVY METAL POLLUTION

Molluscs, including various gastropods and bivalves, have been recognized as a useful tool for monitoring heavy metal contamination in the marine environment. As these organisms are mostly sedentary and bottom dwellers, they accumulate metals in their tissues in proportion to the degree of environmental pollution in both waters and sediments (Conti and Cecchetti, 2003).

Additionally, molluscs exhibit characteristics that make them suitable bioindicators, such as their abundance and wide geographical distribution, relatively longer lifespan, suitable dimensions, and easy identification and collection (Gupta and Singh, 2011).

Bivalves are filter feeders that accumulate metals in their tissues, which reflect the quality and quantity of bioaccumulated chemicals, including heavy metals in their surrounding waters. Since the introduction of the "Mussel Watch" approach by Professor Goldberg of the Scripps Institution of Oceanography in 1975, bivalves are widely used to monitor the spatial and temporal trends of metal contaminations in estuarine and coastal areas.

In response to increasing public and scientific concern about the quality of the marine environment in the Arabian Gulf, the Regional Organization for the Protection of Marine Environment (ROPME) has implemented a regional Mussel Watch Programme.

HEAVY METAL CONCENTRATIONS IN MOLLUSCS FROM THE ARABIAN GULF

Historically, pearl oysters have represented a major marine resource in the Arabian Gulf countries. Pearl fishing in the Arabian Gulf was extensive and represented about 80% of the world's production of natural pearls (Mohammed, 2003). Several studies have been conducted to detect heavy metal contamination in the pearl oyster, *Pinctada radiata*, in the Arabian Gulf.

Buo-Olayan and Subrahmanyam (1997) investigated the contribution of the 1991 oil spill to heavy metal contamination in the marine environment of the Arabian Gulf. Concentrations of Cu, Ni, Pb and Zn were determined in the soft tissue of the gastropod snail *Lunella coronatus* and the pearl oyster, *Pinctada radiata*, collected from coastal stations in Kuwait between 1990 and 1994.

The study noted a significant increase in the levels of Cu, Pb and Zn in both the snail and the oyster samples in 1994. This was primarily attributed to the contribution of the oil spill to the overall load of heavy metals along the Kuwaiti coastline.

Likewise, the levels of heavy metals Cu, Mn, Fe, Zn, Pb, Cd and Ni in the pearl oyster *Pinctada radiata* collected from two oyster beds in Bahrain were determined by Al-Sayed et al. (1994). The study reported elevated levels of Pb and Cd (1.8-14.0 μg g^{-1} wet weight) and (0.4-3.8 μg g^{-1} wet weight), respectively, which exceeded the recommended standards of the World Health Organization (WHO). These high levels were measured in the oysters collected from an offshore station that is subject to navigational activities.

Similarly, Al-Madfa et al. (1998) analyzed the levels of heavy metals Cd, Cu, Pb, Ni and V in the pearl oyster *Pinctada radiata* collected from eight locations around Qatar. Higher concentrations of the investigated metals were generally observed in oysters collected from areas that were subject to intensive dredging activities, continuous shipping traffic and frequent oil pollution. The study reported high mean concentrations of the metals V (4.14 $\pm$ 1.3 μg g^{-1} dry weight), Pb (3.88 $\pm$ 1.1 μg g^{-1} dry weight), and Ni (7.08 $\pm$ 1.6 μg g^{-1} dry weight) which exceeded the international standards.

De Mora et al. (2004) assessed heavy metal contamination in marine bivalves, including pearl oyster *Pinctada radiata* along the eastern coastline of the Arabian Gulf. This study found very high concentrations of Zn (4290 μg g^{-1} dry weight), V (7.3 μg g^{-1} dry weight), and Pb (3.92 μg g^{-1} dry weight) in pearl oysters near the oil refinery in Bahrain.

The marine gastropod *Cerithium scabridum* is abundantly distributed along the coastal and shallow waters and intertidal zones of the Arabian Gulf. Bu-Olayan and Thomas (2001) used this gastropod as a bioindicator to detect heavy metal pollution along the Kuwait coast. Concentrations of the heavy metals Cu, Cr, Pb, Ni, and V were measured in the gills of this gastropod in two seasons during the period 1995-1997. Among the eight sites selected for the study, gastropods collected from Kuwait Bay exhibited the largest concentrations of the measured heavy metals suggesting rapid industrial activities and domestic waste discharges.

Al-Sayed and Dairi (2006) measured the heavy metals Fe, Ni, Zn, Mn, Pb, Cu and Cd in the tissue of the edible marine snail *Turbo coronatus* collected from five nearshore sites around Bahrain. This snail is popular as a seafood delicacy among local people. The study found that the levels of Fe and Cu were higher than equivalent metals reported for snails and other marine organisms in the Arabian Gulf. Additionally, the study found that the levels of Cu and Pb (20.82-35.21 μg g^{-1}) and (1.66-3.03 μg g^{-1}), respectively were higher than the WHO's acceptable limits for marine organisms.

The heavy metals Cd, Pb, Cu, and Zn were measured in the edible clam *Meretrix meretrix* collected from four stations along the coastline of Saudi Arabia (Alyahya et al., 2011). The study showed elevated levels of Pb (1.74 $\pm$ 0.24 and 2.49 $\pm$ 0.27 mg kg^{-1} wet weight) which exceeded the maximum permissible level (1.5 mg kg^{-1} wet weight) recommended by the European Union standards. The study attributed the high concentrations of Pb to the effluent of untreated sewage, fishing boat activities and the oil industry. Despite the slight increase in Pb levels, the study concluded that the clam from the sampling region was within the safe limits for human consumption. Nonetheless, the study stressed the need for long-term monitoring of heavy metals in clam and other marine organisms in order to improve the health risk assessment.

Cephalopoda represents an important component of the world's fisheries. Similarly, the cuttlefish *Sepia pharaonis* is favored among the Saudi Arabian population. Al-Farraj et al. (2011) determined the levels of the heavy metals Cr, Cu, Zn, Ni, Cd, and Pb in the mantle of the cuttlefish *Sepia pharaonis* collected from different fish markets in Al-Khobar City on the Arabian Gulf. The study concluded that the levels of the investigated heavy metals in the cuttlefish were generally low and/or well within the maximum permitted concentrations imposed by different organizations and authorities, and consequently within the safe limits for human consumption.

The concentrations of the heavy metals Cd, Cr, Cu, Hg, Ni, Pb, V, and Zn were measured in various organs of the infaunal clam *Amiantis umbonella* collected from a point source contaminated site influenced by discharges from desalination and power plant, and a reference site in Kuwait Bay (Tarique et al., 2012). This study concluded that mean concentrations of all measured heavy metals were significantly higher in the organs of *Amiantis umbonella* clams collected from the contaminated site in Kuwait Bay compared with clams from the reference site with the exception of Zn in the digestive gland. The study indicated that Zn levels in bivalves do not vary considerably between polluted and unpolluted areas as a result of biological regulation. Several studies reported high levels of heavy metals in areas influenced by land-based activities in Kuwait Bay (Bu-Olayan and Thomas, 2001; Tarique et al., 2012). This is because most of the urban, commercial, industrial and recreational activities are concentrated along Kuwait Bay.

Most of the above studies stressed the need to utilize molluscs as bio-monitors to detect heavy metal contamination in the marine environment of the Arabian Gulf. These studies identified hotspots of heavy metal pollution, which were mainly attributed to anthropogenic sources.

Chapter 6

HEAVY METAL LEVELS IN FISH SPECIES FROM THE ARABIAN GULF

FISH AS BIOINDICATORS FOR HEAVY METAL CONTAMINATION

Characteristics of fish, such as the relatively large body size, long life cycle and the relative ease in maintaining them in the field or the laboratory, make them a favorable bioindicator for heavy metal monitoring. Given that fish species are at the top of the aquatic food chain, they may directly affect the health of humans due to heavy metal bioaccumulation. Therefore, it is important to monitor heavy metal contents in fish bodies to ensure nutritional safety conditions (Zhou et al., 2008).

CONCENTRATIONS OF HEAVY METALS IN FISH SPECIES FROM THE ARABIAN GULF

Fish is important for the economy of the Arabian Gulf countries and it can be considered a major food in the region (Al-Yousuf et al., 2000). Therefore, monitoring levels of heavy metals in fish tissues is critically important.

Al-Sayed et al. (1996) measured the concentrations of Cu, Pb, Zn, Cd, Mn and Ni in the tissues of the grouper fish *Epinephelus coioides* caught from four major fishing grounds in Bahrain. The study reported elevated levels of Pb and Zn (4.3-15.2 μg g^{-1} wet weight) and (223-1253 μg g^{-1} wet weight), respectively, which exceeded the international standards of heavy metal contents in fish.

The concentrations of Pb, Cd, Hg, and As in the tissues of fish and shellfish organisms caught from the coastal areas in Bahrain were determined by Madany et al. (1996). The study indicated that levels of measured heavy metals in these organisms were on the lower side of the international guidelines, apart from As with overall mean levels of 1.7 μg g^{-1} and 3.61 μg g^{-1} for fish and shellfish samples, respectively. The study also showed that fish species caught from the eastern Area of Bahrain were distinguished by higher levels of heavy metals compared with the other studied areas. Even though the eastern area of Bahrain is among the most important fishing grounds in Bahrain, its coastline is heavily occupied with industries, including an oil refinery, an aluminum extrusion factory and desalination plants.

Al-Yousuf et al. (2000) measured the levels of Zn, Cu, Mn and Cd in the liver, skin and muscle tissues of the *Lethrinus lentjan* fish species collected from different sites along the western coast of the United Arab Emirates. This fish is one of the most popular fish in the Arabian Gulf countries and has a commercial importance for over 75% of the population. The study was conducted to compare the levels of heavy metal pollutants before and after the 1991 major oil spill. The study found that the metal levels were generally low or remained constant before and after the oil spill. Further, the study concluded that the concentrations of the measured metals do not constitute a risk factor for human health and appear to be below the permissible limits for human consumption.

The concentrations of Total-Mercury (T-Hg) and Methyl-Mercury (Me-Hg) in the edible muscle tissue of seven fish species collected from Kuwait Bay were measured by Al-Majed and Preston (2000). The selected fish species are of great commercial value in Kuwait and represent different habitats and feeding habits. The study found that around 20.6% of the 330 fish samples analyzed exceeded the WHO permissible limits 0.5 μ g^{-1} and 0.3 μ g^{-1} for T-Hg and Me-Hg, respectively. These elevated levels of T-Hg and Me-Hg were attributed to discharges from petrochemical industries.

Al-Saleh and Shinwari (2002) measured the concentrations of the heavy metals Cd, Pb, Ni, V and As in four fish species (Emperors, Greasy-grouper, Rabbitfish and Doublebar-bream) from three selected sites with agricultural, municipal, and petroleum industrial activities along the eastern coastline of Saudi Arabia. The results of the study showed that the concentrations of Cd, Pb, V, and As were significantly higher in the site influenced by industrial waste discharges than in the other two sites influenced by agricultural and municipal wastes. However, the levels of the studied heavy metals in fish samples from the three sites were below the maximum level permissible in fish for human consumption according to Saudi legislation and European standards.

De Mora et al. (2004) investigated heavy metals in two commercially important fish species; the orange spotted grouper (*Epinephelus coioides*) and the spangled emperor (*Lethrinus nebulosus*). This study reported high levels of Cd (7.19 and 9.94 $\mu g\ g^{-1}$) in the liver of spangled emperor caught from two areas off the coast of the UAE. However, extremely high concentrations of Cd (109 and 195 $\mu g\ g^{-1}$) were found in fish liver from southern Oman. This was attributed to food chain bioaccumulation of high levels of Cd brought into the productive surface waters by the nutrient-rich upwelling in the region.

The levels of Cd, Ni, Pb and V in muscle tissues of three demersal fish species (*Epinephelus coioides*, *Psettodes erumei* and *Solea elongate*) caught from 15 sites along the Iranian coastline of the Arabian Gulf were determined by Pourang et al. (2005). The study found that the mean concentrations of the measured metals in the muscles of the selected fish species were below the international guidelines for human consumption.

Musaiger and D'Souza (2008) analyzed Hg, Pb, Cd and Zn in nine species of raw fish commonly consumed in Bahrain. Even though a maximum concentration of Pb (0.5 $\mu g\ g^{-1}$ wet weight) was reported in one of the fish species (*Liza alata*), the study concluded that the heavy metal content is below the maximum permitted limits and can be safely consumed. Furthermore, a regular monitoring for heavy metals in fish in Bahrain was recommended by the study.

The contents of Al, As, Be, Cd, Cr, Co, Cu, Fe, Pb, Mn, Mo, Ni, Sb, Tl, V and Zn in fish muscles and livers collected from six stations in the Iranian waters of the Arabian Gulf were determined by Agah et al. (2009). The fish samples belonged to five commercially important species; namely, grunt, flathead, greasy-grouper, tiger-tooth croaker and silver pomfret. The study concluded that all of the measured metals in the muscles of the selected fishes were lower than the maximum allowable concentrations, except for arsenic.

The concentrations of Total-Mercury (T-Hg) and Methyl-Mercury (Me-Hg) in the muscle and liver tissues of the abovementioned five fish species that were collected from the Iranian waters of the Arabian Gulf were measured by Agah et al. (2010). According to this study, 3% of the Hg concentrations in fish muscle were higher than 0.5 $\mu g\ g^{-1}$, which corresponds to the maximum acceptable WHO level, while 9% were in the range of polluted fish (between 0.3 and 0.5 $\mu g\ g^{-1}$).

Generally, most of the abovementioned studies demonstrated that heavy metals in fish tissues were within allowable concentrations and pose no threat to public health. However, a regular monitoring of heavy metal levels in fish species is necessary to prevent health risks.

Chapter 7

HEAVY METAL CONCENTRATIONS IN SEAWATERS FROM THE ARABIAN GULF

WHY MONITOR HEAVY METALS IN SEAWATERS?

Globally, there are continuing pressures on the coastal and marine environment from a variety of sources, including industrial and sewage effluents and oil spills.

In the Arabian Gulf, large quantities of effluents, associated with different types of pollutants, including heavy metals, are frequently being discharged to the coastal and marine environments from sewage plants, industrial facilities and desalination plants. Additionally, oil exploration, production, and transportation in the Arabian Gulf are major sources of hydrocarbon pollution in the coastal waters.

Monitoring levels of heavy metals in seawater is important to detect environmental pollution in coastal and marine environments and to ensure that the water quality is suitable for its intended uses (e.g. bathing and recreational waters, desalination process).

Monitoring could also be used to determine trends in the quality of the aquatic environment and how the environment is affected by the anthropogenic release of contaminants (Osman and Kloas, 2010). Likewise, monitoring can be conducted to verify that discharged effluents by waste treatment operations are complying with environmental quality standards set by national, regional or international organizations.

METAL CONCENTRATIONS IN SEAWATERS
OF THE ARABIAN GULF

Al-sayed et al. (1994) measured the concentrations of Cu, Mn, Fe, Zn, Pb, Cd and Ni in seawater samples collected from nearshore and offshore stations in Bahrain. The nearshore station receives treated and untreated domestic effluents from the commercial center of Manama, the capital of Bahrain. The offshore station is located in the shipping lane to Bahrain. The study found no significant differences in heavy metal concentrations in waters from the two stations. The levels of the analyzed heavy metals were on the lower side of the values reported by other studies from unpolluted sites in the Arabian Gulf.

Aboul Dahab and Al-Madfa (1997) investigated the distribution of Cr in seawaters off the eastern coastline of Qatar. Coastal waters off the eastern coastline of Qatar are subjected to several anthropogenic sources of pollution, including leaching from solid waste disposal sites, discharging surface water effluents. The study found that the concentration of Cr in the seawaters reflected the impact of surface water discharge and two harbors in the study area. For instance, relatively elevated Cr concentrations were found in the immediate vicinity of the solid disposal site ($> 3 \ \mu g \ l^{-1}$).

The concentrations of Cu, Fe, Zn, Ni, Pb and Co in seawater were measured in seven locations along the Kuwaiti coastline (Bu-Olayan et al., 2001). Even though no chronic metal contamination was observed, high levels of metals were detected in an area that is influenced by anthropogenic activities.

The concentrations of Cd, Ni, Pb and V in seawater samples collected from different sites along the Iranian coastline were measured by Pourang et al. (2005). The study found that the concentrations of Cd and Pb were below the maximum permissible levels of the standards for the protection of saltwater life.

The Public Commission for the Protection of Marine Resources, Environment and Wildlife in Bahrain is regularly monitoring the quality of territorial waters. Heavy metal contamination in the territorial waters of Bahrain was assessed by analyzing As, Cd, Cu, Fe, Mn, Ni, Pb, V, Zn, and Hg in samples collected from 23 different sites known as fishing areas (Juma and Al-Madany, 2008). Most of the analyzed heavy metals were within the range of the UK quality standards as well as water quality criteria recommended by the US Environmental Protection Agency. However, the concentration of Cu in all sites exceeded the international standards ($4.53 - 119 \ \mu g l^{-1}$). Likewise,

Hg exceeded the international standards in one site located east of Bahrain ($0.38 \ \mu gl^{-1}$), which is heavily occupied by a variety of industrial facilities.

The concentrations of Cd, Cu, Fe, Mn, Pb and Zn were measured in seawaters collected from four beaches in the eastern province of Saudi Arabia (Al-Ghanem, 2010). Elevated levels of Pb and Cu were found associated with beaches influenced by industrial activities. Nonetheless, the study concluded that heavy metal concentrations in the studied sites were within the safe limits.

The above studies indicated that elevated concentrations of heavy metals were localized to areas with high levels of anthropogenic pollution. However, a comparison between the two studies conducted in Bahrain revealed that heavy metals in seawaters were generally higher in the study conducted by Juma and Al-Madany (2008) than those reported by Al-Sayed et al. (1994). This could be attributed to a gradual increase in contaminants over a period of fourteen years separating the two studies.

Similarly, the mean concentrations of Cd, Pb and Ni in the seawater samples from the Iranian coastline of the Arabian Gulf (Pourang et al., 2005) were relatively higher than those reported in Kuwait (Bu-Olayan et al., 2001).

Chapter 8

HEAVY METAL CONCENTRATIONS IN SEDIMENTS FROM THE ARABIAN GULF

MARINE SEDIMENT AS A SINK FOR METAL CONTAMINANTS

With rapid industrialization and urbanization in coastal areas, heavy metals are continuing to be introduced to coastal and marine environments through a variety of sources, including land-based point sources (Ruillian et al., 2008). Heavy metals released to these environments rapidly bind to particulates and sink to the seafloor (Hedge et al., 2009). Therefore, marine sediments act as an ultimate sink for heavy metals introduced into the aquatic environments. The resuspension of sediments due to natural or anthropogenic disturbance can transfer contaminants from the sediment to the water column. Thus, sediments play an important role in the storage and transport of heavy metals (Nobi et al., 2010). Monitoring sediment quality is crucial to maintain a healthy aquatic ecosystem, and ultimately ensure good protection of human health (Osman and Kloas, 2010). Therefore, measuring levels of heavy metals in marine sediments is widely used in monitoring and assessment programmes.

HEAVY METAL CONCENTRATIONS IN SEDIMENTS FROM THE ARABIAN GULF

Basaham and Al-Lihaibi (1993) measured the concentrations of Cr, Cu, Co, Ni, V, Zn, Mn and Fe in sediments along the western coastline of the

Arabian Gulf. This study was conducted to assess the extent of pollution in sediments after the 1991 oil spill. Sediment samples were collected from the nearshore area between Kuwait and Qatar, which generally showed a trend of increasing particle-size from the north to the south of the Arabian Gulf. The analyzed metals were high in the mud samples collected off the Kuwaiti coast and decreased to the south as the sand fraction increased. This finding was attributed to the higher capacity of fine-grained sediments to associate with heavy metals. The study reported elevated levels in all measured heavy metals off the Kuwaiti coast in comparison with studies conducted in the same region in the early '80s (Anderlini et al., 1982). However, these levels were within the range published in literature from unpolluted areas. This study concluded that heavy metal concentrations in the sediments of the Arabian Gulf showed a spread of values that were related to variable sediment compositions, indicating a minimal effect of anthropogenic input upon the absolute concentration of heavy metals.

The heavy metal contents of the bottom sediments in the Arabian Gulf were determined in 1992 by Al-Abdali et al. (1996) in order to assess the impact of the 1991 Kuwaiti oil slick. The study indicated that all chronic concentrations of heavy metals, apart from elevated levels of Fe in the north-western area due to river transport, were within the permissible natural background levels in the Arabian Gulf, including the oil-polluted areas off Saudi Arabia and Bahrain, which were directly affected by the Kuwaiti oil spill. The study concluded that the 1991 Kuwaiti oil slick had a minimal effect on the state of pollution by heavy metals in the Arabian Gulf.

The effects of land-based industrial pollution were assessed by measuring the concentrations of Pb, Zn, Cd, and V in sediments collected from nineteen coastal stations in Bahrain (Akhter and Al-Jowder, 1997). The study detected elevated concentrations of Pb (33.9-343.1 mg kg^{-1}) in heavily industrialized areas. The study also indicated a trend of increasing levels of most of the investigated heavy metals in areas located near industries.

Shriadah (1998) measured the concentrations of Cd, Co, Cr, Cu, Mn, Ni, Pb and Zn in sediment samples collected from five different creeks along the Arabian Gulf coast of the United Arab Emirates. The study found that most of the investigated metals exhibited a common trend of increase towards the inner parts of the creek where they receive increasing quantities of municipal and industrial wastewaters from many outlets. Additionally, elevated levels of heavy metals were found in creeks associated with high inputs of municipal wastewaters and effluents from other land-based activities. Desalination plants in the Arabian Gulf are the major source of potable water (Naser, 2011a).

Effluents from these desalination plants that contain elevated levels of heavy metals are discharged directly to the marine environment of the Arabian Gulf (Sadiq, 2002). Al-Ketbi et al. (1993) distinguished three sources of heavy metals in the reject waste water of desalination plants; 1) concentrated seawater-borne heavy metals, 2) heavy metals associated with scale inhibitors as components or contaminants, and 3) corrosion of permeator tubes or other utility pipes.

Sadiq (2002) assessed the contamination of marine sediments due to heavy metals associated with reject water discharges from a seawater desalination plant on the eastern coastline of Saudi Arabia. The study found very high concentrations of Cd, Co, Cu, Hg, V, Fe and Zn in sediment samples from the immediate vicinity of the outfall of the desalination plants. However, these elevated concentrations decreased progressively away from the outfall, suggesting a localized pollution in that area.

An assessment of contamination in marine sediment due to heavy metals in the Arabian Gulf was conducted during 2000-2001 (De Mora et al., 2004). Heavy metals Al, V, Cr, Mn, Fe, Co, Ni, Cu, Zn, As, Ag, Cd, Sb, Hg and Pb were measured in nearshore sediments collected from Bahrain, Qatar, United Arab Emirates (UAE) and Oman. Sediment metal loadings were generally lower or comparable to those previously reported in the Arabian Gulf (Fowler et al., 1993). However, the study noted two hot spots of heavy metals in Bahrain and on the east coast of the UAE. Elevated levels of heavy metals Cu, Hg, Pb, and Zn with maximum concentrations of 48.3, 0.22, 99.0, and 52.2 µg g^{-1} dry weight, respectively, were recorded off the oil refinery in Bahrain. This localized anthropogenic pollution was attributed to the industrial effluents from the refinery and other industries located on the eastern coastline in Bahrain. Higher concentrations of heavy metals Co, Cr, and Ni were reported at Akkah beach on the east coast of the UAE with maximum concentrations of 45, 303, and 1010 µg g^{-1} dry weight, respectively, and attributed to the metal-rich mineralogy of the region.

The levels of Cd, Ni, Pb and V in sediment samples collected from subtidal areas off the Iranian coastline of the Arabian Gulf were measured by Pourang et al. (2005). The study concluded that the concentrations of Cd, Pb and Ni in the sediments (2.9, 90.5 and 64.9 µgg^{-1} dry weigh, respectively) were notably higher than global baseline values.

Assessment of contaminants in the Dubai coastal region, United Arab Emirates, was conducted by Al-Darwish et al. (2005). This study measured the concentrations of Ba, Cr, Cu, Mn, Ni, Pb, Sr, V and Zn in sediment samples collected from Dubai coastal zone. The study reported elevated levels of Cu,

Ni and Zn in comparison with background levels of unpolluted sediments in the Arabian Gulf. The highest concentrations of these metals were found in chronically polluted areas, suggesting that they were closely associated and were derived from pollutant sources.

Zyadah and Almoteiry (2012) measured the concentrations of Cu, Zn, Pb, Cd and As in sediment samples collected from the coastline of the Eastern Province, Saudi Arabia. Elevated levels of metals were found in areas influenced by drainage of waste waters from sewage outlets and other land-based activities.

Generally, studies indicated that levels of heavy metals in the Arabian Gulf are within the natural background levels found in other offshore areas. However, elevated levels of heavy metals are associated with land-based anthropogenic activities such as oil refiners and desalination pants.

Chapter 9

MACROBENTHIC COMMUNITY STRUCTURE AS A BIOINDICATOR FOR HEAVY METAL CONTAMINATION

MACROBENTHIC ASSEMBLAGES AS INDICATORS FOR BIOTIC INTEGRITY OF MARINE ECOSYSTEMS

Soft-sediment intertidal and subtidal marine environments are characterized by high levels of diversity and productivity (Gray 1997). These marine habitats are widely subjected to anthropogenic disturbance and pollution (Airoldi and Beck 2007) and the macrobenthic assemblages inhabiting these environments may respond through changes in their community structures (Gray 1989). Accordingly, soft-bottom benthic communities are reliable indicators of the biotic integrity of marine ecosystems (Ryu et al., 2011).

Macrobenthos are a species-rich group of invertebrates that are mainly composed of polychaetes, crustaceans, molluscs, and many other taxonomic groups (Snelgrove, 1998). Polychaetes occur in almost all benthic marine sediments, and are typically the dominant component of macrobenthos in terms of the number of species and abundance (Hutchings, 1998). Similarly, crustaceans and molluscs constitute diverse taxonomic groups that inhabit all major marine habitats (Snelgrove, 1998).

Macrobenthic assemblages provide a useful tool for detecting environmental pollution and disturbance because these organisms are relatively long-lived and sedentary, and hence reflect the ambient conditions of sediments (Rappe, 2010; Ryu et al., 2011; De Jonge et al., 2012), in which many contaminants, including heavy metals, are ultimately partitioned (Hedge et al., 2009).

These organisms consist of different species that show different levels of tolerance to stresses and pollution. They can exhibit detectable changes in their community structure in response to stresses and pollution, such as changes in biodiversity, abundance, biomass, and numerical dominance of opportunistic species (Gray, 1989).

Macrobenthic assemblages are widely used as bioindicators to detect environmental pollution and as a tool for monitoring programmes and ecological assessment studies (Salas et al. 2006). They may also be utilized to characterize the 'health' of coastal and marine ecosystems represented by their structures (the species and populations involved) and functions (the flow of energy, growth and productivity) (Boesch and Paul, 2001).

CHARACTERIZATION OF HEAVY METAL POLLUTION USING MACROBENTHOS IN THE ARABIAN GULF

Given that more than 97% of the bottom substrate of the Arabian Gulf is dominated by sand and mud (Al-Ghadban, 2002), macrobenthos form the largest and most diverse marine ecosystem. Therefore, macrobenthic assemblages are considered an effective tool to detect environmental contamination, including heavy metals.

Bu-Olayan and Thomas (2005) investigated the use of diversity indices in benthic assemblages as indicators for heavy metal pollution in Kuwait Bay. Species diversity, evenness and dominance indices were determined, and the levels of Cu, Zn, Fe and Ni in organisms were measured. The study showed that relatively high levels of ecological indices (species diversity, evenness and dominance) were found in sites with low trace metal levels. The study concluded that macrobenthic assemblages could be utilized as an effective tool to detect heavy metal pollution in the coastal and marine environments of the Arabian Gulf.

The community structure of macrobenthos inhabiting a subtidal area subject to effluents containing hydrocarbons and heavy metals from the main oil refinery and other industrial facilities on the eastern coastline of Bahrain was investigated by Naser (2010b). The study recorded 44 species of which polychaetes, molluscs, crustaceans and other groups accounted for 66.0%, 22.7%, 6.8% and 4.5%, respectively. The elimination of sensitive species such as crustaceans and a reduction in their diversity levels might be considered as adverse consequences of heavy metal pollution. The impacts of heavy metals are reflected in the limited number of species and abundance of crustaceans in the area influenced by the industrial effluents in Bahrain.

Similarly, reduced levels of crustacean diversity and abundance in areas off the eastern coastline affected by heavy metal inputs from a wide range of industrial activities in Bahrain were reported by Al-Wedaei et al. (2011). The study reported that crustaceans only accounted for 5% of the total benthic community population in the eastern coastline compared with 39% in the western coastline of Bahrain. This reduction in crustacean assemblages was primarily attributed to anthropogenic pollution, including heavy metals.

The abovementioned studies demonstrated that macrobenthic assemblages can be used as an effective tool to detect and monitor environmental pollution due to heavy metal contamination. Indeed, studying macrobenthic assemblages that are naturally under extreme physical conditions may provide insight into mechanisms of adaption to anthropogenic pollution and disturbance.

Chapter 10

Spatial Distribution of Heavy Metals in Marine Sediments Influenced by Land-Based Anthropogenic Sources in Bahrain: A Case Study

Why Conduct the Case Study?

Heavy metals are considered a major anthropogenic contaminant of coastal and subtidal marine habitats that may lead to the degradation of ecosystems (Ansari et al., 2004; Ruilian et al., 2008). Heavy metals in seawater and marine sediments are incorporated into the aquatic food webs and then biomagnified at higher trophic levels (Hosono et al., 2011). Therefore, heavy metal pollution is a major concern for both the environment and human health (Joksimovic et al., 2011).

Naturally, heavy metals could be introduced to the marine environments through atmospheric deposition, leaching of soils, and erosion (Kennish, 2001). Anthropologically, coastal and marine environments are susceptible to the input of heavy metals due to industrial and sewage effluents, discharges from desalination plants, ports and shipping activities, and the mobilization of sediments associated with dredging and reclamation (Akhter, 1990; Fowler et al., 1993; Nayar et al., 2004; Hashim and Hajjaj, 2005; Miri and Chouikhi, 2005).

Heavy metal contamination in coastal and marine environments is becoming an increasingly serious threat in the Arabian Gulf (De Mora et al., 2010), which is considered among the highest anthropogenically impacted regions in the world (Halpern et al., 2008). Therefore, monitoring the spatial distribution of heavy metals in the vicinity of land-based anthropogenic sources is critically required.

Like the rest of the Arabian Gulf countries, Bahrain is witnessing a rapid industrialization and economic development. Therefore, Bahrain was selected as a case study from the Arabian Gulf countries to monitor the gradient of heavy metal contamination resulting from land-based anthropogenic activities.

CHARACTERIZING ANTHROPOGENIC SOURCES OF HEAVY METALS IN BAHRAIN

As discussed in previous chapters, the Arabian Gulf is naturally stressed due to marked fluctuations in sea temperatures and high salinities, and additional anthropogenic input of heavy metals could arguably be critical for its marine ecosystems (Akhter and Al-Jowder, 1997). The coasts of the Arabian Gulf are subject to intensive dredging and reclamation activities, and pollution from various land-based sources (Sheppard et al., 2010).

Likewise, Bahraini coastal and marine environments are subject to anthropogenic activities that may contribute significantly to the overall load of heavy metal pollution (Figure 10.1).

Dredging and disposal activities induce changes in environmental conditions in the impacted sites, which may affect the mobility of associated heavy metals (Tack et al., 1998; Berg et al., 2001; Guevara-Riba et al., 2004).

Bahraini coastal and marine environments are the prime target for most of the major housing, recreational, and economic projects, which are typically associated with intensive dredging and reclamation activities (Naser, 2011b). Industrial and sewage effluents are widely recognized as major sources of heavy metal inputs to aquatic environments (Nyamangara et al., 2008). Bahrain has witnessed a rapid industrial growth, mainly in the sectors of oil refining, aluminum and petrochemical industries. Several companies and industrial factories are producing effluents that may contain hydrocarbons, and heavy metals. It is estimated that around 1, 714, 410 m^3 day^{-1} of industrial effluents are discharged to the shallow subtidal areas (Table 10.1).

Sewage effluents are a major source of coastal pollution in Bahrain. Several sewage treatment plants, varying in size and the degree of treatment, are discharging effluents to the coastal and subtidal areas in Bahrain. The main one is Tubli Water Pollution Control Centre (TWPCC), which discharges around 160 000 m^3 day^{-1} of treated effluents into the shallow water of Tubli Bay. Nuidrat sewage treatment plant contains a series of aeration pounds and discharges around 7000 m^3 day^{-1} of effluents directly into the mangrove swamps in the Ras-Sand area in Tubli Bay.

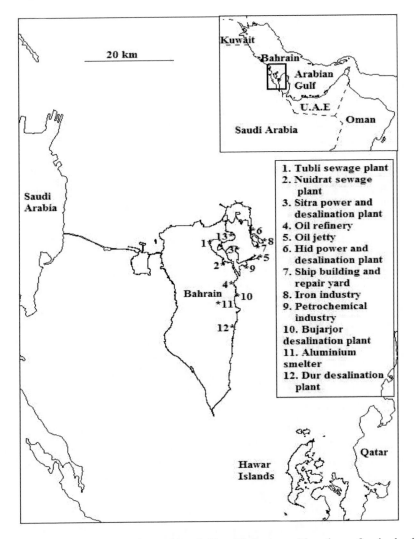

Figure 10.1. Maps showing the Arabian Gulf and Bahrain, and locations of major land-based anthropogenic activities contributing to heavy metals enrichment in coastal and marine environments in Bahrain.

Table 10.1. Major industrial facilities that discharge effluents into the marine environment in Bahrain (Naser, 2010a)

Factory/Company	Activity	Effluent m3day^{-1}
Bahrain Petroleum Company	Oil refining	700 000
Aluminum Bahrain	Aluminum smelter	4 000
Aluminum Extrusion Company	Aluminum extrusions	350
Gulf Aluminum Rolling Mills	Aluminum sheets and coils	150 000
Gulf Petrochemical Industry	Ammonia, methanol, urea	850 000
Gulf International Company	Iron industry	60
Arab Ship building and Repair Yard	Ship repair dry dock	10 000
Total		1 714 410

Bahrain, like most of the Arabian Gulf countries, depends mainly on desalination seawater as a source of potable water. In Bahrain, there are currently four major desalination plants producing fresh water and energy. Sitra Power and Water Station (SPWS) is the largest plant in Bahrain, with a capacity of 125 megawatts of electrical power and 25 million gallons per day of desalinated water using multi-stage flash technology (Khalaf and Redha, 2001). SPWS produces around 66000 m^3 day^{-1} of effluent to the marine environment of which 12000 m^3 are brine water. This brine water causes an average increase in temperature of 7.5 °C above the natural water temperatures of summer and winter (Altayaran and Madany, 1992). Bujarjor desalination plant produces 46 000 m^3 day^{-1} of drinking quality water by desalination brackish groundwater based on the reverse osmosis technique. The quantity of effluents being discharged into the marine environment is estimated to be around 1134 m^3 day^{-1} (Khalaf and Redha, 2001).

The Arabian Gulf is considered the largest reserve of oil in the world. Consequently, Bahrain is under a permanent threat from oil-related pollution. The sources of oil spills are offshore oil wells, underwater pipelines, oil tanker incidents, oil terminals, loading and handling operations, weathered oil and tar balls, and the illegal dumping of ballast water (Literathy et al., 2002).

AIM OF THE STUDY

Sediments act as important sinks of heavy metals in coastal and marine environments (Berg et al., 2001). Sediments have frequently been analyzed for monitoring purposes and for detecting sources of pollution in aquatic environments (Nyamangara et al., 2008). This study, therefore, aims to:

1) determine the concentrations of selected heavy metals; namely, lead (Pb), zinc (Zn), copper (Cu), and cadmium (Cd) in marine sediments influenced by land-based anthropogenic activities.
2) investigate heavy metal distributions in subtidal areas influenced by industrialized coastal zone.
3) establish a baseline information for the current status of heavy metal contamination in Bahrain.

MATERIALS AND METHODS

Site Selection

Tubli Bay and subtidal areas off the eastern coastline of Bahrain were selected to investigate heavy metal concentrations due to land-based anthropogenic activities such as reclamation and dredging, industrial and sewage effluents, brine water discharge from desalination plants, and oil pollution. The marine area of Tubli Bay has been reduced during the last decade due to extensive reclamation activities. Two major sewage treatment plants are discharging treated and partially treated sewage into the bay. The eastern coastline of Bahrain is heavily occupied by industrial facilities including an oil refinery, aluminum smelter, and desalination plants.

Sampling Design

Samples were collected subtidally in a transect design. This approach in sampling is suitable to detect the inshore-offshore gradient of heavy metal concentrations due to point source discharges and other land-based anthropogenic activities (Figure 10.2). Transects locations and orientations were selected based on the characteristics of the investigated anthropogenic activities. This approach of sampling could form the basis for the long-term monitoring of sources, pathways and extents of heavy metal pollution in coastal and marine environments. Sediment samples were collected from five transects (hereinafter T1, T2, T3, T4 and T5). Transects were divided into ten stations with an equal distance between each one and the next (250 m).

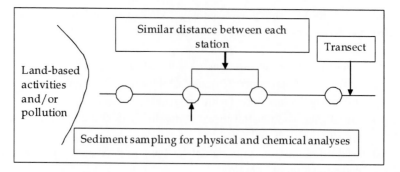

Figure 10.2. Sampling design of sediments in an inshore-offshore orientation based on the source of activity or pollution; namely, sewage and industrial effluents and brine wastewater discharge.

The selected sampling transects may be divided into three types based on sources of impacts:

- Sites affected by sewage effluents from Tubli and Nudirat sewage treatment plants, reclamation impacts and coastal modification (T1 and T2).
- Sites affected by a major power and desalination plant (Sitra plant), port, navigational channel, and shipbuilding and repairing yard (T3).
- Sites affected by industrial effluents from major industries such as oil refinery, petrochemical and aluminum factories, and desalination plants (T4 and T5).

Sediment Sampling and Analyses

Environmental factors such as depth (m), salinity (PSU), and seawater temperature (^{o}C) were measured at each station using a GARMIN FishFinder 240, ATAGO refractometer, and a thermometer, respectively. Sediment samples were collected from a boat using hand operated Van Veen grab, transferred into polyethylene and stored under ice. At the laboratory, samples were stored at -10 ^{o}C until the treatment phase. Sediment samples were analyzed physically (organic content and grain size analysis), and chemically (sediment digestion and analysis of the selected heavy metals).

Approximately 50g of homogenized sediment were sieved on a mechanical sieve shaker (KARL KOLB) through six sieves (mesh sizes from 0.038–2 mm). The weight of sediment fraction in each sieve was obtained.

Another portion of the homogenized sample was used to obtain the organic content of the sediment by incinerating a known weight at a temperature of 450°C for 12 hours. The difference in weight before and after ashing was obtained, and the percentage of organic content (ash-free dry weight) was determined.

Microwave-assisted digestion was conducted using a MARS5 microwave (CEM Corporation, USA). The digestion was performed according to US-EPA 3051 methods. Harbor sediment (LGC6156) from the Laboratory of the Government Chemist, UK, was used as a reference material for quality assurance (metals recovery 93.1 - 98.3 %). The chemical reagents used in the digestion were analytical grade 'AnalaR' from VWR Chemicals. The samples were analyzed for zinc, cadmium, lead, and copper using the voltammetry technique (Metrohm® 757 VA computrace) and following Metrohm Application Bulletin No. 231/2e.

RESULTS

Physical Conditions and Sediment Characteristics

Generally, salinity levels ranged between 44-46 PSU reflecting typical high salinities in the Arabian Gulf. However, localized reduction in salinity levels was recorded in stations 1 and 2 of T1 (37 and 42 PSU, respectively) due to the low salinity of wastewater associated with domestic sewage effluents. Similarly, an increase in salinity was observed in station 1 of T3, which is likely due to the brine wastewater discharge from the power and desalination plant.

A substantial increase in surface seawater temperature was recorded in station 1 of T3. A difference of 14°C was measured at a distance of 250m from the outlet of the power and desalination plant. It is evident that this increase in seawater temperature around the outlet is attributed to the brine wastewater that is associated with high temperatures.

The first five stations and station 7 of T1 were characterized by accumulated organic matter due to the continued discharge of sewage effluents. Additionally, the last three stations of the same transect were composed of hard substrate. Only station 6 was physically and chemically analyzed. Consequently, T1 was eliminated from the overall analyses of heavy metal concentrations. The substrates of stations 1-4 of T3 were mainly coarse sand mixed with patches of gravels and small stones. Conversely, most of the remaining stations of T3 were composed of fine or very fine sand, which are associated with the navigational channel leading to the nearby port. Transect T4 was mostly composed of fine sand, while T5 ranged from medium to fine sand.

Table 10.2. Environmental measurements and sediment characteristics of T1, T2 and stations 1-5 of T3

Transect	Station	Salinity (PSU)	Temperature (°C)	Depth (m)	Mean gain size (Ø)	Description	% Organic content
1	1	37	17	0.8	-	Organic matter	100
	2	42	16	5.4	-	Organic matter	100
	3	44	15	8.3	-	Organic matter	100
	4	44	15	9.2	-	Organic matter	100
	5	45	14	10.8	-	Organic matter	100
	6	44	14	4.2	2.40	Fine sand	2.23
	7	45	14	8.6	-	Organic matter	90
	8	45	14	2.5	-	hard substrate	-
	9	45	15	1.9	-	hard substrate	-
	10	45	15	3.5	-	hard substrate	-
2	1	44	13	1.5	2.00	Medium sand	2.38
	2	44	14	1.6	2.09	Fine sand	3.84
	3	44	14	2.9	2.54	Fine sand	2.99
	4	44	14	2.6	3.55	Very fine sand	8.59
	5	44	14	2.5	3.73	Very fine sand	4.01
	6	45	15	2.5	3.40	Very fine sand	3.06
	7	45	15	2.4	3.30	Very fine sand	4.95
	8	45	15	2.5	1.79	Medium sand	2.68
	9	45	15	3.0	2.26	Fine sand	2.77
	10	45	15	5.0	-	hard substrate	-
3	1	46	30	5.7	-	hard substrate	-
	2	45	16	0.7	-	hard substrate	-
	3	45	16	0.9	-	hard substrate	-
	4	45	17	3.3	0.23	Coarse sand	2.67
	5	45	16	7.5	2.66	Fine sand	4.03

Table 10.3. Environmental measurements and sediment characteristics of stations 6-10 of T3, T4, and T5

Transect	Station	Salinity (PSU)	Temperature (°C)	Depth (m)	Mean gain size (Ø)	Description	% Organic content
	6	45	16	10.8	2.77	Fine sand	4.7
	7	45	16	9.9	3.19	Very fine sand	6.36
3	8	45	16	8.3	2.10	Fine sand	4.71
	9	45	15	8.5	2.47	Fine sand	4.52
	10	45	15	7.9	3.40	Very fine sand	4.96
	1	45	15	1.3	2.23	Fine sand	3.96
	2	45	15	1.9	2.24	Fine sand	5.90
	3	45	15	4.0	2.25	Fine sand	4.24
	4	45	15	5.0	1.08	Medium sand	3.55
4	5	45	15	5.5	1.68	Medium sand	2.19
	6	46	15	5.3	2.07	Fine sand	2.93
	7	46	15	5.9	2.78	Fine sand	3.82
	8	46	15	6.4	2.71	Fine sand	3.91
	9	46	15	6.8	2.88	Fine sand	4.81
	10	46	15	5.9	2.40	Fine sand	3.68
	1	45	15	1.4	1.38	Medium sand	2.21
	2	45	15	2.6	1.38	Medium sand	2.00
	3	45	15	3.0	2.45	Fine sand	4.52
	4	45	15	2.5	0.82	Coarse sand	2.99
5	5	45	14	4.5	1.27	Medium sand	2.28
	6	45	14	6.0	3.26	Very fine sand	2.46
	7	45	14	5.9	3.35	Very fine sand	2.34
	8	45	14	5.9	3.36	Very fine sand	2.60
	9	45	14	5.9	3.42	Very fine sand	3.82
	10	45	14	5.6	3.45	Very fine sand	4.33

The organic content in the sediment ranged between 2.00 – 8.59% with an overall mean of 3.79%. However, variation among transects was observed. T2, T3, T4, and T5 ranged between 2.38-8.59, 2.67-6.36, 2.19-5.90 and 2.0-4.52% with means of 3.90, 4.56, 3.89 and 2.99%, respectively. Details of environmental measurements and sediments' characteristics are presented in Tables 10.2 and 10.3.

Spatial Gradient of Heavy Metal Contaminations

Transect sampling design was adopted to detect onshore-offshore spatial gradient of heavy metals. Generally, concentrations of zinc and copper showed fluctuations through stations, and no clear trend of onshore-offshore gradient was detected (Figures 10.3 and 10.4).

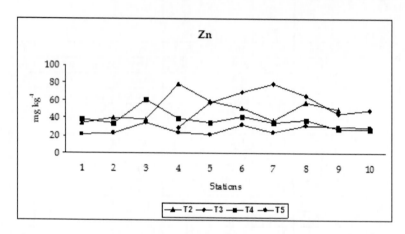

Figure 10.3. Concentration of zinc in stations of T2, T3, T4 and T5, with no clear onshore-offshore gradient.

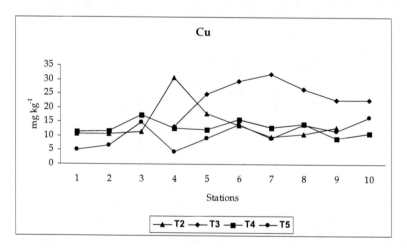

Figure 10.4. Concentration of copper in stations of T2, T3, T4 and T5, with no clear onshore-offshore gradient.

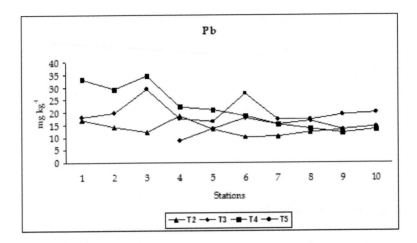

Figure 10.5. Concentration of lead in the stations of T2, T3, T4 and T5, with a clear seaward decrease in the stations of T4.

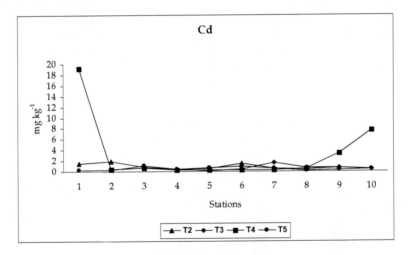

Figure 10.6. Concentration of cadmium in stations of T2, T3, T4 and T5, with a significant increase in stations 1, 9 and 10 of T4.

Conversely, T4 showed a clear seaward decrease in lead concentrations (Figure 10.5). A localized increase in cadmium concentration was recorded in station 1 of T4 adjacent to the outlet of Bujarjor desalination plant with a concentration of 19.14 mg kg^{-1}. Similarly, higher concentrations of cadmium were detected in stations 9 and 10 of the same transect (3.35 and 7.64 mg kg^{-1}, respectively) (Figure 10.6).

Mean Concentrations of Heavy Metals in Sampling Sites

Substantial increases in the mean concentrations of zinc and copper in T3 were observed reflecting the anthropogenic input associated with brine wastewater discharge and navigational activities in the nearby port.

Mean concentrations of cadmium and lead were higher off the eastern coastline compared with Tubli Bay (T1 and T2) reflecting industrial activities along the eastern coastal areas (Figure 10.7).

Variation of Metal Concentrations in Comparison with Regional and International Guidelines

Comparison between metal concentrations in Bahrain and the Canadian sediment quality guidelines revealed that the overall mean concentration of cadmium significantly exceeded the interim sediment quality guideline. Indeed, the maximum concentration of cadmium (19.14 mg kg^{-1}) was three times higher than the probable effect level, above which adverse biological effects are usually or always observed. Apart from cadmium, heavy metal concentrations of this study were within the range of variations that are reported in sediments from the Arabian Gulf (Table 10.4).

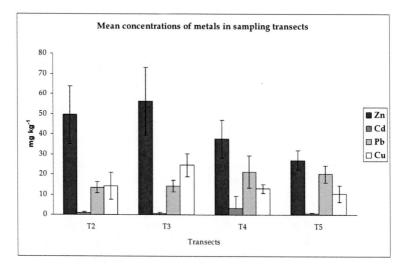

Figure 10.7. Heavy metal concentrations in sampling transects; error bar (T2: n = 9, T3: n = 7, T4 and T5: n = 10).

Table 10.4. Comparison between metal concentrations in Bahrain and the Canadian sediment guidelines, 1 (ISQG): interim sediment quality guideline, 2 (PEL): probable effect level, above which adverse biological effects are usually or always observed (CCME, 2001); 3 range of metal concentrations reported in sediments from the Arabian Gulf (ROPME, 2003)

| Metal mg kg -1 | Bahrain | | Canadian Standards | | Arabian Gulf |
	Mean	Range	ISQG[1]	PEL[2]	Range[3]
Pb	17.43	8.59 - 34.58	30.2	112	0.20 – 64.30
Cu	14.67	4.25 – 31.98	18.7	108	1.30 – 142.0
Zn	40.99	20.94 – 78.90	124	271	0.70 – 410.3
Cd	1.37	0.083 – 19.14	0.7	4.2	0.01 – 4.5

DISCUSSION

Although some trace metals are essential biological elements for aquatic organisms, all the metals could be potentially toxic when certain threshold concentrations are exceeded (Ansari et al., 2004). The metals that were analyzed in the present study could be broadly arranged according to increasing level of toxicity from lead, zinc, copper, to cadmium (Abel, 1996). Lead is toxic to animals and humans. It can accumulate in individual organisms as well as the entire food chain. Lead can physiologically and neurologically affect humans. Zinc is essential for plants, animals and humans. However, excessive quantities of zinc may lead to acute or chronic toxicity. Copper is an essential micronutrient required in the growth of plants and animals. In humans it contributes to the production of blood hemoglobin. In large doses, copper is toxic and excessive ingestion can destroy red blood cells. Cadmium is a very toxic metal and has been responsible for a number of deaths (Abel, 1996; Kennish, 2001).

After entering the marine environment either naturally or anthropogenically, heavy metals are distributed among water, biotic and sediment compartments. Sediment distribution is influenced by biological, chemical and physical properties of the sediment (De Gregori et al., 1996). It is widely recognized that fine sediments often contain higher metal levels than the coarser grained sediments (Al-Abdali et al., 1996; Belzunce et al., 2001; Garcia et al., 2008). Similarly, this study showed a correlation between the heavy metal concentrations and the particle size of the sediment and its organic content.

It is recognized that heavy metals are a by-product from the desalination process due to corrosion (Mohamed et al., 2005; Lattemann and Hopner, 2008a). Mean concentrations of Zn and Cu were elevated near the main desalination plant in Bahrain (SPWS). Similarly, a significant increase in Cd concentration which exceeded the limits of national and international standard guidelines was detected near the outlet of the Bujarjor desalination plant. Such localized increase in Cd due to desalination plants was similarly reported in the Arabian Gulf with a maximum concentration of 31.59 mg kg^{-1} (Sadiq, 2002).

Heavy metals Pb, Cu, Zn, and Cd are associated with the oil industry, and are toxic to organisms due to bioaccumulation (Munawar et al., 2002). Adeniyi and Afolabi (2002) reported elevated concentrations of heavy metals in soil within the vicinity of facilities handling refined petroleum products. The eastern coastline is recognized as a hotspot for high concentrations of hydrocarbons and heavy metals (De Mora et al, 2004). Indeed, the shallow subtidal area off the oil refinery is considered to be chronically polluted (De Mora, 2010).

Localized hotspots have been reported for Cu, Pb and Zn in Bahrain, which were mainly attributed to petroleum industries (De Mora et al., 2004, 2010). The effect of industrial effluents was reflected in the present study through the increase in the mean concentrations of Cd and Pb off the eastern coastline in Bahrain (T4 and T5).

Concentrations of heavy metals in the Arabian Gulf were generally found to be comparable to uncontaminated offshore continental shelf areas, reflecting natural background levels (Basaham and El-Sayed, 1998). However, ROPME (2003) indicated that elevated concentrations of metals in the Arabian Gulf are mainly associated with sediments from impacted areas adjacent to harbors and industrial facilities. Likewise, this study detected a localized contamination of Cd that is attributed to the industrial land-based effluents.

Sources of heavy metal pollution in Bahrain are not limited to sewage and industrial effluents, but extend to other activities such as dredging and reclamation.

It is widely documented that mobilization and concentration of heavy metals increase after dredging and reclamation activities (Singh et al., 1998; Guerra et al., 2009; Hedge et al., 2009). In light of the current escalation in coastal reclamation and development in Bahrain, such activities are considered a main source for mobilizing heavy metals.

CONCLUSION

Heavy metals are anthropologically introduced to the Bahraini coastal and marine environments through a variety of sources and activities, including sewage and industrial effluents, brine discharges and coastal modifications. This study detected localized hotspots of metal contamination that could be attributed to industrial pollution. Metal contamination in Bahrain is a major threat to the environment and to human health. Therefore, continuous spatial and temporal monitoring is critically needed for the better management of coastal and marine environments in Bahrain.

Chapter 11

MANAGEMENT OF HEAVY METALS IN THE ARABIAN GULF

WHY IS MANAGEMENT OF HEAVY METAL POLLUTION IN THE ARABIAN GULF CRITICALLY REQUIRED?

Prevention and controlling heavy metal contamination is a global concern (Williams, 1996); many countries are initiating plans to combat heavy metal pollution.

The characteristics of the Arabian Gulf as a shallow, semi-enclosed basin that is subject to intensive anthropogenic activities make it susceptible to heavy metal pollution.

The impact of heavy metal pollution is not limited to vulnerable and naturally stressed ecosystems of the Arabian Gulf, but extends to human health and the safety of food resources.

Effective management of heavy metal pollution necessitates identifying sources of contamination, the nature of affected ecosystems and the nature of human risks (Islam and Tanaka, 2004; Van Lavieren et al., 2011).

Therefore, measures that could help in the control and prevention of heavy metal pollution in the Arabian Gulf are suggested.

These measures can be broadly classified into three main categories; 1) environmental management approaches represented by Environmental Impact Assessment (EIA), 2) national and regional environmental laws and regulations, and 3) scientific research and technology.

ENVIRONMENTAL IMPACT ASSESSMENT (EIA)

Environmental Impact Assessment (EIA) is a systematic process of identifying, predicting, evaluating and mitigating the environmental consequences of a proposed project on the biological and physical environments (Glasson et al., 2005). EIA aims at integrating environmental considerations into the decision-making system, minimizing or avoiding adverse impacts, protecting natural systems and their ecological processes, and implementing principles of sustainable development (IAIA, 1999).

EIA is considered a standard tool for decision-making in most countries throughout the world (Erickson, 1994). It ensures that authorities are provided with the necessary knowledge relating to any likely significant effects of a proposed project on the environment prior to the decision-making process. The integration of environmental considerations may result in a rational and structured decision-making process that maintains a balance of interest between the development action and the environment (Glasson et al., 2005). EIA minimizes or avoids the adverse effects of a proposed development on the environment by addressing effective designs, alternatives, mitigations, cumulative impacts, and monitoring (Cooper and Sheate, 2002).

EIA, as an environmental management tool, can contribute to heavy metal management in two ways; 1) reducing the amount of heavy metal pollutants generated by industrial processes such as seawater desalination, sewage treatment, oil refining; 2) minimizing heavy metals' mobilization due to dredging and reclamation activities in coastal and marine environments.

Human and economic developments through securing infrastructure facilities and industrial projects are major priorities in the Arabian Gulf countries (Naser, 2010b). This is associated with rapid population growth that requires more potable water, wastewater treatment facilities and energy services. Desalination remains the most feasible alternative to meet the future needs of freshwater supply in the Arabian Gulf countries (Dawoud and Al-Mulla, 2012). Therefore, the construction of new desalination plants is continuously undertaken on the coastline of the Arabian Gulf. Similarly, new sewage treatment plants are being constructed, and existing oil refineries are being upgraded or expanded.

One fundamental role of EIA is altering the design or the process of the proposed project in order to avoid or reduce the predicted environmental impacts (Cooper and Sheate, 2002). Therefore, EIA can play an important role in reducing the amount of pollutants, including heavy metals, generated from industrial processes.

EIA is increasingly being applied to assess and predict the environmental effects of existing or proposed desalination plants (Hoepner, 1999; Elabbar and Elmabrouk, 2005; ROPME, 2005a; Elabbar, 2008; Lattemann and Hoepner, 2008aandb; Tsiourtis, 2008; UNEP, 2008). EIA studies revealed that corrosion is a main source of heavy metals associated with effluents from desalination plants (UNEP, 2008). For instance, several heavy metals, including copper, nickel, chromium and zinc, could be discharged to the marine environment from thermal desalination plants as a result of corrosion in the heat exchanger alloys (Hoepner, 1999). Therefore, mitigation measures to reduce corrosion during the desalination process should be addressed in EIA studies.

These may include using appropriate materials such as stainless steel with high corrosion resistance, or non-metallic material, including concrete or plastic to minimize corrosion (Lattemann and Hoepner, 2008a and b; UNEP, 2008). Reducing corrosion during the desalination process is reflected positively on the economic and environmental interests.

EIA is widely recognized as a measure to address the environmental impacts associated with oil industry projects (Alemagi, 2007). Heavy metals including chromium, iron, nickel, copper, molybdenum, selenium, vanadium and zinc are typically associated with petroleum refinery wastewaters (Wake, 2005).

EIA could be applied on a project level such as a new oil refinery (Jaber and Probert, 1999), or on the whole sector of the oil industry (Alam et al., 2010). Refining technologies that minimize environmental impacts should be adapted either for new or existing refineries. For instance, Bahrain Petroleum Company (BAPCO) has upgraded its facilities to produce unleaded gasoline in 2000. Similarly, technologies might be applied to reduce the levels of pollutants, including heavy metals, associated with industrial wastewater effluents.

Heavy metals are among the most common toxicants associated with sewage discharges. Approaches and technologies that may reduce heavy metal inputs from sewage treatment plants should be investigated in EIA studies (ROPME, 2005b). Mitigation measures in EIA studies should also explore the environmental feasibility of proposed locations of treatment plants. For instance, the largest sewage treatment plant in Bahrain is discharging effluents to the shallow bay with limited water flushing.

Intensive dredging and reclamation activities in the Arabian Gulf are, directly or indirectly, contributing to the heavy metal loads in coastal and marine environments (Naser, 2012a). Dredging and reclamation processes may induce changes in environmental conditions in the impacted sites, which may affect the mobility of associated heavy metals (Guevara-Riba et al., 2004). Changes in heavy metal concentrations may potentially affect the flora, fauna and bird populations in contaminated sites. Additionally, major dredging activities may interfere with underground reservoirs, which increases the risk of heavy metal contamination.

Therefore, it is of crucial importance to determine heavy metal concentrations in both dredging and reclamation sites in EIA studies (Lee et al., 2010).

Adopting and applying environment-friendly methods and technologies of sediment dredging and disposal may minimize the release of pollutants, including heavy metals, into the marine environments (Allsop, 2002). For instance, silt curtains are widely used to reduce the suspended sediment associated with dredging and reclamation activities (Netzband and Adnitt, 2009).

However, the planning of dredging and reclamation activities is typically carried out in the Arabian Gulf on a project-by-project basis, without assessing environmental impacts strategically. This approach may ignore the cumulative impacts of coastal reclamation on the valued ecosystem components and important fishery resources that occur in an additive or interactive manner (Noble, 2010).

Therefore, maintaining sustainable use of coastal and marine natural resources in the Arabian Gulf requires measures to holistically address the interactions among the several reclamation and dredging activities and their additive and cumulative impacts, including heavy metal pollution.

Strategic Environmental Assessment (SEA) as an important tool toward ensuring sustainability is increasingly becoming incorporated into international policy-making (Dalal-Clayton and Sadler, 2004). SEA has emerged as an important element in the environmental decision-making process in developed countries, including Europe and North America (Clark, 2008). However, SEA is still relatively new in developing countries (Fischer, 2007). SEA may be conducted in response to major plans such as reclamation and dredging in the Arabian Gulf.

SEA may ensure that environmental consequences of reclamation and dredging activities are identified and assessed, including heavy metal mobilization, before the implementation phase. SEA may contribute to strengthening the current EIA systems, and delivering the principles of sustainable development into the coastal and marine policy in the Arabian Gulf (Naser, 2012b).

NATIONAL AND REGIONAL ENVIRONMENTAL LAWS AND REGULATIONS

Environmental legislations related to the prevention of pollution in the Arabian Gulf are based on a range of national laws and regulations as well as regional and international agreements. Nationally, there are several framework laws with respect to protecting the environment and combating environmental pollution in each country (Khan and Price, 2002):

- The Decree establishing the Environmental Protection Committee in Bahrain (1980);
- The Law protecting the Environment in Kuwait (1980);
- The Act for Environmental Protection and Pollution Control in Oman (1979);
- Environmental Protection Standards in Saudi Arabia (1982);
- The Decree establishing the Supreme Committee for Environment in United Arab Emirates (1981).

These framework laws facilitated the implementation of related regional and international regulations and agreements (Khan and Price, 2002). Several regulations dealing with heavy metal pollution have been developed in most of the countries of the Arabian Gulf. Notably, environmental quality standards for selected heavy metals in wastewater effluents have been adopted in the Arabian Gulf countries (Table 11.1).

Regionally, the Kuwait Regional Convention for Cooperation on the Protection of the Marine Environment from Pollution (Kuwait Convention), which was adopted in 1978, provides the basis for an integrated regional response to combating pollution (Khan, 2008). The Regional Organization for the Protection of the Marine Environment (ROPME) was established under the Kuwait Convention to act as a focal point for regional cooperation (Khan and Price, 2002). Land-based sources of pollution are major contributors to heavy metal loads in the Arabian Gulf (chapter 3). One of the four Protocols under Kuwait Convention, Protocol for the Protection of the Marine Environment against Pollution from land-based sources, adopted in 1990, addresses the pollution of the marine environment from land-based anthropogenic activities and proposes criteria for their management (Khan and Price, 2002; Khan, 2008).

Internationally, Arabian Gulf countries are members of several international environmental agreements concerned with the protection of marine environments from pollution (El-Habr and Hutchinson, 2008). Nonetheless, there is a recognized need for the further enforcement of legislations and regulations related to the environment in the Arabian Gulf. Indeed, a strengthening in the laws and regulations has resulted in a decline in the levels of heavy metal pollutants in coastal bays in the Philippines and Indonesia (Hosono et al., 2010, 2011). Hosono et al. (2010) investigated the heavy metal pollution history in the marine sediments of Manila Bay, Philippines.

Table 11.1. Industrial effluent standards for selected heavy metals in the Arabian Gulf (mgl^{-1}) (ROPME, 2005a)

Element	Bahrain		Kuwait	Oman	Qatar	Saudi Arabia
	Monthly Average *	Maximum Value **	Standard	Standard	Standard	Standard
Aluminum	15	25	5	5	15	
Antimony			1.0			
Arsenic	0.1	0.5	0.1	0.1	0.1	0.1
Barium			2.0	2.0	2.0	
Beryllium			0.1	0.3		
Boron			0.75	1.0	1.5	
Cadmium	0.01	0.05	0.01	0.01	0.05	0.02
Chromium	0.1	1.0	0.2	0.05	0.01	0.1
Cobalt			0.2	0.05	0.2	
Copper	0.2	0.5	0.2	0.2	0.2	0.2
Cyanide	0.05	0.1	0.1	0.1	0.0	0.05
Iron	5.0	10	5.0	1.5	1.0	
Lead	0.2	1.0	0.5	0.1	0.1	0.1
Lithium			2.5	0/07		
Mercury	0.001	0.005	0.001	0.001	0.001	0.001
Manganese			0.2			
Molybdenum			0.01	0.05		
Nickel	0.2	0.5	0.2	0.1	0.2	0.2
Selenium				0.02		
Silver			0.1	0.01		
Vanadium			0.1	0.1		
Zinc	2.0	5.0	2.0	1.0	0.5	1.0

* Average reading during 30 days.

** Maximum value must not be exceeded at any time.

The study indicated that the rate of decline in heavy metal pollution increased after the implementation of stricter environmental regulations. Likewise, Hosono et al. (2011) observed a decline in heavy metal concentrations in the sediments of Jakarta Bay, Indonesia. The study attributed this decline to the stricter environmental regulations which were enforced at the end of the 1990s.

SCIENTIFIC RESEARCH AND TECHNOLOGY

Applying scientific research and utilizing the latest technology related to heavy metal management are integral parts of any effort to prevent environmental pollution in the Arabian Gulf.

Scientific investigation of the heavy metal pathways, uptaking mechanisms, speciation in seawater and sediments, and responses of marine organisms to heavy metal contamination, particularly when these organisms thrive in harsh environmental conditions like those in the marine environment of the Arabian Gulf, is fundamental to the implementation of prevention and remediation strategies.

For a broader picture of heavy metal pollution and bioaccumulation patterns in the Arabian Gulf, a holistic spatial and temporal environmental monitoring is required. Such an integrated monitoring approach may include measuring levels of heavy metals in seawaters, sediments and marine organisms.

Several logistical and technical limitations may hinder the effective monitoring of heavy metals in the Arabian Gulf. Therefore, further cooperation between local and regional institutions and organizations concerned with scientific research and monitoring of heavy metals in the Arabian Gulf is required. For example, the Regional Organization for the Protection of the Marine Environment (ROPME) may play an important role in coordinating the efforts of combating and monitoring heavy metal pollution in the Arabian Gulf.

Applying best available technologies and approaches in dealing with heavy metal pollution is recognized as an essential strategy in heavy metal management (ROPME, 2005a and b). There are several methods and techniques that might be utilized to eliminate or reduce heavy metal pollution from contaminated environments (Chen et al., 2009; Hashim et al., 2011; Sdiri et al., 2012). Among the most effective methods used for metal reduction are phytoremediation (Chu et al., 2012), ecoremediations (Bulc and Slak, 2009), biosorption (Davis et al., 2003; Soltmann et al., 2010), and bioremediation using certain types of bacteria (Naik et al., 2012). Likewise, molecular, biochemical, or cellular biomarkers have been recently utilized to detect metal contamination in marine organisms. Biomarkers may contribute to detecting, quantifying and understanding the significance of exposure to pollutants, including heavy metals, in the marine environment (Picado et al., 2007). Additionally, biomarkers may be utilized to assess and predict the human health risks due to environmental pollution (Torres et al., 2008).

Chapter 12

CONCLUSION AND RECOMMENDATIONS

Marine organisms and ecosystems in the Arabian Gulf are naturally and anthropogenically stressed. Despite these extreme environmental conditions, the Arabian Gulf supports a variety of important ecosystems such as seagrass beds, coral reefs, mangroves and mudflats that contribute to the productivity of marine resources.

Rapid industrialization and urbanization along the coastlines of the Arabian Gulf contributes to the heavy metal loads in the coastal and marine environments. The Arabian Gulf is susceptible to heavy metal pollution due to anthropogenic effluents from sewage treatment plants, industrial facilities, and desalination plants. Additionally, sediment mobilization due to intensive dredging and reclamation activities, and frequent incidents of major and minor oil spills are major sources of heavy metal contamination in the Arabian Gulf.

The heavy metal levels in various types of living organism from the Arabian Gulf have been investigated by several researchers. Algal species have been used as bioindicators for heavy metal contamination along the coasts of the Arabian Gulf. While some studies have indicated that heavy metals in algal species were on the lower side of the values reported by other studies in oceanic areas and estuaries (Kureishey, 1991; El-Sayed and Dorgham 1994), subsequent studies in the Arabian Gulf have detected a trend of increasing metal concentrations, suggesting evidence of contamination from anthropogenic sources (Kureishey et al., 1995; Buo-Olayan and Subrahmanyam, 1996; Mohamed, 2002; Al-Homaidan, 2006, 2007). Elevated levels of heavy metals are progressively recorded in algal species influenced by sources of anthropogenic pollution.

Molluscs are increasingly used to monitor heavy metal pollution in the Arabian Gulf. Studies suggested that levels of heavy metals are similar or lower in several species of molluscs compared to other regions (Buo-Olayan and Subrahmanyam, 1997; Bu-Olayan and Thomas, 2001; Alyahya et al., 2011; Al-Farraj et al., 2011; Tarique et al., 2012). However, hotspots of heavy metal contamination were identified in localized areas influenced by oil pollution from refiners and intensive dredging and reclamation activities. Elevated levels of heavy metals that exceeded recommended international standards were reported in pearl oysters *Pinctada radiata* in Bahrain (Al-Sayed et al., 1994; De Mora et al., 2004), and in Qatar (Al-Madfa et al., 1998).

Fish is a major source of food in the Arabian Gulf countries. Most of the relevant studies concluded that heavy metals in fish tissues were within allowable concentrations and pose no threat to public health (Al-Sayed et al., 1996; Madany et al. 1996; Al-Yousuf et al., 2000; Al-Majed and Preston, 2000; Al-Saleh and Shinwari, 2002; De Mora et al., 2004; Pourang et al., 2005; Musaiger and D'Souza, 2008; Agah et al., 2009, 2010). However, some studies reported levels of metals that exceeded the WHO permissible limits (Al-Sayed et al., 1996; De Mora et al., 2004; Agah et al., 2010). Therefore, regular monitoring of heavy metal levels in fish species is necessary to prevent health risks and to ensure nutritional safety conditions.

Monitoring levels of heavy metals in seawater is important to detect environmental pollution in coastal and marine environments and to ensure that the water quality is suitable for its intended uses. This is of critical importance in the Arabian Gulf as seawaters are used in desalination processes and for recreational activities. Concentrations of heavy metals in seawaters in the Arabian Gulf were found to be relatively low, reflecting unpolluted environmental conditions (Al-sayed et al., 1994; Bu-Olayan et al., 2001; Pourang et al. 2005; Al-Ghanem, 2010). However, detectable elevations in metal concentrations were reported in areas influenced by land-based discharges (Aboul Dahab and Al-Madfa, 1997; Juma and Al-Madany, 2008).

Marine sediments act as an ultimate sink for heavy metal input in marine environments. The majority of the studies conducted in the Arabian Gulf suggests that levels of heavy metals in sediments are similar or lower compared to other regions (Basaham and Al-Lihaibi, 1993; Fowler et al., 1993). However, high concentrations of heavy metals have been reported along Saudi and Kuwaiti shores following the 1991 Gulf War (Al-Arfaj and Alam 1993). Elevated levels of heavy metals have been detected in localized areas influenced by industrial facilities (Akhter and Al-Jowder, 1997), desalination plants (Sadiq, 2002), and oil refineries (De Mora, 2004).

It is recognized that the cumulative information available on the levels of heavy metals in living organisms, seawaters and sediments is generally patchy and does not provide a complete picture of their spatial and temporal distribution in the Arabian Gulf. Therefore, there is a critical need for a holistic approach to monitor heavy metal concentrations and distributions, and a comprehensive strategy to combat and manage heavy metal pollution.

The case study (chapter 10) provides a systematic spatial monitoring approach for detecting metal contamination due to land-based anthropogenic sources. This study initially characterized the anthropogenic sources of heavy metals in Bahrain, which include dredging and reclamation, sewage effluents, desalination discharges, industrial wastewaters, and oil spills. The study also established a spatial sampling design to facilitate the detection of pollution gradients. The findings of this study showed an onshore-offshore spatial gradient of heavy metals, and identified localized increases in heavy metals near outfalls of desalination plants and industrial facilities. Continuous spatial monitoring may help in establishing management strategies for heavy metal pollution in the Arabian Gulf.

Heavy metal management strategies can be classified into immediate and long-term measures. The immediate actions may include formulating quality guidelines and standards, enforcing existing national and regional environmental regulations and laws, and conducting holistic environmental monitoring programmes.

Long-term measures may include applying EIA to existing and proposed projects or activities that may contribute to heavy metal pollution, building capacity for advancing scientific research, and using the latest technological approaches and techniques in the prevention and remediation of heavy metal pollution.

EIA may play an important role in altering or modifying the process, design, and technology of industrial facilities and consequently minimizing the risks and impacts of heavy metal pollution. EIA should also allow for best practices in dredging and reclamation activities to reduce the risk of metal pollution due to sediment mobilization.

Building capacity toward scientific research in the field of environmental pollution is important in order to investigate the mechanisms governing ecosystems' resistance and adaption to heavy metal pollution in the Arabian Gulf. Indeed, the Arabian Gulf is increasingly receiving international scientific attention to study the effects of environmental extremes on marine organisms, and to predict the likely impacts of future climate change on the ecological integrity of marine ecosystems.

REFERENCES

Abdel-Kareem, M. (2009). *New algal records from the Arabian Gulf coast of Saudi Arabia.* Botany Research International, 2 (4): 268-276.

Abdulqader, E. (1999). The role of shallow waters in the life cycle of the Bahrain penaeid shrimps. *Estuarine, Coastal and Shelf Science*, 49: 115-121.

Abdulqader, E., Miller, J. (2012). Marine turtle mortalities in Bahrain territorial waters. *Chelonian Conservation and Biology*, 11:133-138.

Abel, P. (1996). Water pollution biology. Taylor and Francis, London.

Aboul Dahab, O., Al-Madfa, H. (1997). Chromium distribution in waters and sediments of the eastern side of the Qatari Peninsula. *The Science of the Total Environment*, 196: 1-11.

Adeniyi, A., Afolabi, J. (2002). Determination of total petroleum hydrocarbons and heavy metals in soils within the vicinity of facilities handling refined petroleum products in Lagos metropolis. *Environment International*, 28: 79-82.

Agah, H., Leermakers, M., Elskens, M., Fatemi, S., Baeyens, W. (2009). Accumulation of trace metals in the muscle and liver tissues of five fish species from the Persian Gulf. *Environmental Monitoring and Assessment*, 157: 499-514.

Agah, H., Leermakers, M., Gao, Y., Fatemi, S., Katal, M., Baeyens, W., Elskens, M. (2010). Mercury accumulation in fish species from the Persian Gulf and in human hair from fishermen. *Environmental Monitoring and Assessment*, 169: 203-216.

Airoldi, L., Beck, M. (2007). Loss, status and trends for coastal marine habitats of Europe. *Oceanography and Marine Biology: An Annual Review*, 45: 345–405.

Akhter, S. (1990). Trace metal analysis of sewage sludge and soils in Bahrain. *Water, Air and Soil Pollution*, 51: 147-152.

Akhter, M., Al-Jowder, O. (1997). Heavy metal concentrations in sediments from the coast of Bahrain. *International Journal of Environmental Health Research*, 7: 85-93.

Al-Abdali, F., Massoud, M., Al-Ghadban, A. (1996). Bottom sediments of the Arabian Gulf-III: Trace metal contents as indicators of pollution and implications for the effect and fate of the Kuwait oil slick. *Environmental Pollution*, 93: 285-301.

Alam, J., Ahmed, A., Munna, G., Ahmed, A. (2010). Environmental impact assessment of oil and gas sector: A case study off Magurchara gas field. *Journal of Soil Science and Environmental Management*, 1 (5): 86-91.

Allan, S. Ramirez, C., Vasquez, J. (2008). Effects of dredging on subtidal macrobenthic community structure in Mejillones Bay, Chile. *International Journal of Environment and Health*, 2: 64-81.

Al-Arfaj, A., Alam, I. (1993). Chemical characterization of sediments from the Gulf area after the 1991 oil spill. *Marine Pollution Bulletin*, 27: 97-101.

Al-Darwish, H., El-Gawad, Mohammed, F., Lotfy, M. (2005). Assessment of contaminants in Dubai coastal region, United Arab Emirates. *Environmental Geology*, 49: 240-250.

Alemagi, D. (2007). The oil industry along the Atlantic coast of Cameroon: Assessing impacts and possible solutions. *Resources Policy*, 32: 135-145.

Al-Farraj, S., El-Gendy, A., Alyahya, H., El-Hedeny, M. (2011). Heavy metals accumulation in the mantle of the common cuttlefish Sepia pharaonis from the Arabian Gulf. *Australian Journal of Basic and Applied Sciences*, 5: 897-905.

Al-Ghadban, A. (2002). Geological oceanography of the Arabian Gulf. In: *The Gulf ecosystem: Health and Sustainability*, N. Khan, M. Munawar and A. Price (Eds.), pp. 23-39, Backhuys Publishers, Leiden.

Al-Ghanem, W. (2010). Water and *Ceratophllum demersum* analyses in Al-Jubail, East Saudi Arabia. *Journal of the Arabian Aquaculture society*, 5 (1): 35-44.

Al-Homaidan, A. (2006). Brown algae as bioindicators of heavy metal pollution along Saudi coast of the Arabian Gulf. *Saudi Journal of Biological Sciences*, 13: 99-103.

Al-Homaidan, A. (2007). Heavy metal concentrations in three species of green algae from the Saudi coast of the Arabian Gulf. *International Journal of Food, Agriculture and Environment*, 5 (3-4): 354-358.

Ali, A., Hamed, M., Abd El-Azim, H. (2011). Heavy metals distribution in the coral reef ecosystems of the Northern Red Sea. *Helgoland Marine Research,* 65: 67-80.

Al-Ketbi, F., Isnasious, E., Al-Mohyas, A. (1993). Practical observations on reserve osmosis plants including raw water contamination problems, different intake station and permeator performance. *Desalination,* 93: 259-272.

Allsop, N. (2002). *Breakwater, coastal structures and coastlines.* Institute of Civil Engineers, UK.

Al-Khayat, J. (2007). Macrofauna abundance in seagrass of Qatari waters, Arabian Gulf. *Egyptian Journal of Aquatic Research,* 33: 257-276.

Al-Madfa, H., Abdel-Moati, M., Al-Gimaly, F. (1998). *Pinctada radiata* (pearl oyster): a bioindicator for metal polltion monitoring in the Qatari waters (Arabian Gulf). *Bulletin of Environmental Contamination and Toxicology,* 60: 245-251.

Al-Majed, N., Preston, M. (2000). An assessment of the total and methyl mercury content of zooplankton and fish species tissue collected from Kuwait territorial waters. *Marine Pollution Bulletin,* 40: 298-307.

Al-Muzaini, S., Beg, M., Muslamani, K. and Al-Mutairi, M. (1999). The quality of marine water around a sewage outfall. *Water Science and Technology,* 40(7): 11-15.

Al-Saleh, I., Shinwari, N. (2002). Preliminary report on the levels of elements in four fish species from the Arabian Gulf of Saudi Arabia. *Chemosphere,* 48: 749-755.

Al-Sayed, H., Dairi, M. (2006). Metal accumulation in the edible marine snail *Turbo coronatus* (Gmelin) from different locations in Bahrain. *Arab Journal of Scientific Research,* 24: 48-57.

Al-Sayed, H., Al-Saad, J., Madany, I., Al-Hooti, D. (1996). Heavy metals in the grouper fish *Epinephelus coioides* from the coast of Bahrain: an assessment of monthly and spatial trends. *International Journal of Environmental Studies,* 50: 237-246.

Al-Sayed, H., Mahasneh, A., Al-Saad, J. (1994). Variation of trace metal concentrations in seawater and pearl oyster Pinctada radiata from Bahrain (Arabian Gulf). *Marine Pollution Bulletin,* 28 (6): 370-374.

Al-Sayed, H., Naser, H., Al-Wedaei, K. (2008). Observations on macrobenthic invertebrates and wader bird assemblages in a tropical marine mudflat in Bahrain. *Aquatic Ecosystem Health and Management,* 11: 450-456.

Al-Tisan, I., Chandy, J. (1995). Distribution of heavy metals in plankton collected during the Umitaka Matu cruise (II) in the ROPME sea area.

Umitaka Maru symposium, Tokyo. Japan, December, 1995. pp 1287-1294.

Altayaran, A., Madany, I. (1992). Impact of desalination plant on the physical and chemical properties of seawater, Bahrain. *Water Research*, 26: 435-441.

Al-Wedaei, K., Naser, H., Al-Sayed, H., Khamis, A. (2011). Assemblages of macro-faun associated with two seagrass beds in Kingdom of Bahrain: Implications for conservation. *Journal of the Association of Arab Universities for Basic and Applied Sciences*, 10: 1-7.

Al-Yamani, F., Rao, D., Nharzi, A., Ismail, W., Al-Rifaie, K. (2006). Primary production off Kuwait, an arid zone environment, Arabian Gulf. *International Journal of Oceans and Oceanography*, 1(1): 67-85.

Alyahya, H., El-Gendy, A., Al Farraj, S., El-Hedeny, M. (2011). Evaluation of heavy metal pollution in the Arabian Gulf using the clam *Meretrix meretrix* Linnaeus, 1758. *Water, Air and Soil Pollution*, 214: 499-507.

Al-Yousuf, M., El-Shahawi, M., Al-Ghais, S. (2000). Trace metals in liver, skin and muscle of *Lethrinus lantjan* fish species in relation to body length and sex. *The Science of the Total Environment*, 256: 87-94.

Anderlini, V., Mohammed, O., Zebra, M., Fowler, S., Mirmand, P. (1982). Trace metals in marine sediments of Kuwait. *Bulletin of Environmental Contamination and Toxicology*, 28: 75-80.

Ansari, T., Marr, I., Tariq, N. (2004). Heavy metals in marine pollution perspective-a mini review. *Journal of Applied Sciences*, 4: 1-20.

Areiqat, A. Mohamed, K. (2005). Optimization of the negative impact of power and desalination plants on the ecosystem, *Desalination*,185:95-103.

Barth, H., Khan, N. (2008). Biogeophysical setting of the Gulf. In: A. Abuzinada, H. Barth, F. Krupp, B. Boer, T. Al-Abdessalam (eds.), *Protecting the Gulf's Marine Ecosystems from Pollution*. Birkhauser, Switzerland.

Basaham, A., El-Sayed, M. (1998). Distribution and phase association of some major and trace elements in the Arabian Gulf sediments. *Estuarine, Coastal and Shelf Science*, 46: 185-194.

Basaham, A., Al-Lihaibi, S. (1993). Trace elements in sediments of the western Gulf. *Marine Pollution Bulletin*, 27: 103-107.

Basson, P. (1992). Checklist of marine algae of the Arabian Gulf. *Journal of the University of Kuwait* (Science), 19: 217-230.

Bayen , S. (2012). Occurrence, bioavailability and toxic effects of trace metals and organic contaminants in mangrove ecosystems: A review. *Environment International*, 48: 84-101.

Belzunce, M., Solaun, O., Franco, J., Valenica, V., Borja, A. (2001). Accumulation of organic matter, heavy metals and organic compounds in surface sediments along the Nervion Estuary (Northern Spain). *Marine Pollution Bulletin*, 42: 1407-1411.

Berg, G., Meihers, G., Heijdt, L., Zwolsan, J. (2001). Dredging-related mobilization of trace metals: a case study in the Netherlands. *Water Research*, 35: 1979-1986.

Blackmore, G., Morton, B., Huang, Z. (1998). Heavy metals in *Balanus amphitrite* and *Tetraclita squamosa* (Crustacea: Cirripedia) collected from the coastal waters of Xiamen, China. *Marine Pollution Bulletin*, 36: 32-40.

Boesch, D., Paul, J. (2001). An overview of coastal environment health indicators. *Human and Ecological Risk Assessment*, 7: 1409-1417.

Bulc, T., Slak, A. (2009). Ecoremedations- a new concept in multifunctional ecosystem technologies for environmental protection, *Desalination*, 246: 2-10.

Buo-Olayan, A., Subrahmanyam, M. (1996). Heavy metal in marine algae of the Kuwait coast. *Bulletin of Environmental Contamination and Toxicology*, 57 (5): 816-832.

Buo-Olayan, A., Subrahmanyam, M. (1997). Accumulation of copper, nickel. Lead and zinc by snail, *Lunella coronatus* and pearl oyster, *Pinctada radiata* from the Kuwait coast before and after the Gulf war oil spill. *The Science of the Total Environment*, 197: 161-165.

Bu-Olayan, A., Thomas, B. (2001). Heavy metal accumulation in the gastropod, *Cerithium scabridum* L., from the Kuwait coast. *Environmental Monitoring and Assessment*, 68: 187-195.

Bu-Olayan, A., Al-Hassan, R., Thomas, B. (2001). Trace metal toxicity to phytoplankton of Kuwait coastal waters. *Ecotoxicology*, 10: 185-189.

Bu-Olayan, A., Thomas, B. (2005). Validating species diversity of benthic organisms to trace metal pollution in Kuwait Bay, off the Arabian Gulf. *Applied Ecology and Environmental Research*, 3 (2): 93-100.

Campanella, L., Cubadda, F., Sammartino, M., Saoncella, A. (2000). An algal biosensor for the monitoring of water toxicity in estuarine environments. *Water Research*, 35 (1): 69-76.

Carpenter, K., Krupp, F., Jones, D. and Zajonz, U. (1997). The living marine resources of Kuwait, eastern Saudi Arabia, Bahrain, Qatar and the United Arab Emirates: *FAO Species identification field guide for fishery purposes*. Food and Agriculture Organization of the United Nations, Rome.

CCME (2001). *Canadian sediment quality guidelines for the protection of aquatic life.* Canadian Council of Ministries of the Environment, Winnipeg.

Chen, M., Tang, Y., Li, X., Yu, Z. (2009). Study on the heavy metals removal efficiencies of constructed wetlands with different substrates. *Journal of Water Resource and Protection,* 1: 22-28.

Chu, L., Shao, H., Sun, J., Xu, G., Zhang, L., Yan, K. (2012). Some advances in bio-removing hazardous heavy metals from contaminated soil. In: S. Hong-Bo (ed.), *Metal contamination: Sources, detection and environmental impact.* NOVA Science Publishers, New York, pp. 19-40.

Clark, N. (2008). *The international law of environmental impact assessment: process, substance and integration.* Cambridge University Press, Cambridge.

Coles, S., McCain, J. (1990). Environmental factors affecting benthic communities of the western Arabian Gulf. *Marine Environmental Research,* 29: 289-315.

Conti, M., Cecchetti,G. (2003). A biomonitoring study: trace metals in algae and molluscs from Tyrrhenian coastal areas. *Environmental Research,* 93: 99-112.

Cooper, L., Sheate, W. (2002). Cumulative effect assessment: a review of UK environmental impact statements. *Environmental Impact Assessment Review,* 22: 415-439.

Dalal-Clayton, B. Sadler, B. (2004). *Strategic environmental assessment: A sourcebook and reference guide to international experience.* IIID, London.

Davis, T., Volesky, B., Mucci, A. (2003). A review of the biochemistry of heavy metal biosorption by brown algae. *Water Research,* 37: 4311-4330.

Dawoud, M., Al-Mulla, M. (2012). Environmental impacts of seawater desalination: Arabian Gulf case study. *International Journal of Environment and Sustainability,* 1: 22-37.

De Gregori, I., Pinochet, H., Arancibia, M., Vidal, A. (1996). Grain size effects on trace metals distribution in sediments from two coastal areas of Chile. *Bulletin of Environmental Contamination and Toxicology,* 57: 163-170.

Defew, L., Mair, J., Guzman, H. (2005). An assessment of metal contamination in mangrove sediments from Punta Mala Bay, Pacific Panama. *Marine Pollution Bulletin,* 50: 574-552.

DeForest, D. Brix, K. Adams. W. (2007). Assessing metal bioaccumulation in aquatic environments: The inverse relationship between bioaccumulation factors, trophic transfer factors and exposure concentration. *Aquatic Toxicology*, 84: 236-246.

De Jonge, M., Belpaire, C., Geeraerts, C., De Cooman, W., Blust, R., Bervoets, L. (2012). Ecological impact assessment of sediment remediation in a metal-contaminated lowland river using translocated zebra mussels and resident macroinvertebrates. *Environmental Pollution*, 171:99-108.

De Mora, S., Fowler, S., Wyse, E., Azemard, S. (2004). Distribution of heavy metals in marine bivalves, fish and coastal sediments in the Gulf and Gulf of Oman. *Marine Pollution Bulletin*, 49: 410-424.

De Mora, S., Tolosa, I., Fowler, S., Villeneuve, J., Cassi, R., Cattini, C. (2010). Distribution of petroleum hydrocarbons and organochlorinated contaminants in marine biota and coastal sediments from the ROPME Sea Area during 2005. *Marine Pollution Bulletin*, 60: 2323-2349.

Duarte, C. (2002). The future of seagrass meadows. *Environmental Conservation*, 29 (2): 129-206.

Duffy, J. (2006). Biodiversity and the functioning of seagrass ecosystems. *Marine Ecology Progress Series*, 311: 233-250.

Elabbar, M., Elmabrouk, F. (2005). Environmental impact assessment for desalination plants in Libya. Case study: Benghazi North and Tobrouk desalination plants. *Desalination*, 185: 31-44.

Elabbar, M. (2008). The Libyan experimental on the environmental impact assessment for desalination plants. *Desalination*, 220: 24-36.

El-Habr, H., Hutchinson, M. (2008). Efforts of regional and international organization in reducing levels of pollution in the Gulf. In: Abuzinada, A., Barth, H., Krupp, F., Boer, B., Al Abdessalaam, T. (eds), *Protecting the Gulf's marine ecosystems from pollution*. Birthauser, Verlag/Switzerland, pp. 93-106.

El-Sayed, M., Dorgham, M. (1994). Trace metals in macroalgae from the Qatari coastal water. *Journal King Abdulaziz University: Marine Sciences*, 5: 13-24.

Erftemeijer, P., Shuail, D. (2012). Seagrass habitats in the Arabian Gulf: distribution, tolerance thresholds and threats. *Aquatic Ecosystem Health and Management*. 15(S1): 73-83.

Erickson, P. (1994). *A practical guide to environmental impact assessment*. Academic Press, London.

Farkas, A., Salanki, J., Varanks, I. (2003). Crustaceans as biological indicators of heavy metal pollution in Lake Balaton (Hungary). *Hydrobiologia*, 506-509: 359-364.

Fischer, T. (2007). *Theory and Practice of Strategic Environmental Assessment: Toward a more systematic approach.* Earthscan, UK.

Fowler, S., Readman, J., Oregioni, B., Villeneuve, J., McKay, K. (1993). Petroleum hydrocarbons and trace metals in nearshore Gulf sediments and biota before and after the 1991 war: an assessment of temporal and spatial trends. *Marine Pollution Bulletin*, 27: 171-182.

Fu, F., Wang, Q. (2011). Removal of heavy metal ions from wastewaters: A review. *Journal of Environmental Manag*ement, 92: 407-418.

Garcia, E., Cruz-Motta, J., Farina, O., Bastidas, C. (2008). Anthropogenic influences on heavy metals across marine habitat in the western coast of Venezuela. *Continental Shelf Research*, 28: 2757-2766.

Giusti, L. (2001). Heavy metal contamination of brown seaweed and sediments from the UK coastline between the Wear river and the Tees river. *Environmental International*, 26: 275-286.

Glasson, J., Therivel R., Chadwick, A. (2005). *Introduction to Environmental Impact Assessment.* Spon Press, London.

Gray, J. (1989). Effects of environmental stress on species rich assemblages. *Biological Journal of the Linnean Society*, 37, 19–32.

Gray, J. (1997). Marine biodiversity: Patterns, threats and conservation needs. *Biodiversity and Conservation*, 6, 153–175.

Guerra, R., Pasteris, A., Ponti, M. (2009). Impacts of maintenance channel dredging in a northern Adriatic coastal lagoon. I: Effects on sediment properties, contamination and toxicity. *Estuarine, Coastal and Shelf Science*, 85: 134-142.

Guerra-Garcia, J., Ruiz-Tabares A., Baeza-Rojano, E., Cabezas, M., Diaz-Pavon, J., Pacios, I., Maestre, M., Gonzalez, A., Espinosa, F., Garcia-Gomez, J. (2010). Trace metals in *Caprella* (Crustacea: Amphipoda). A new tool for monitoring pollution in coastal areas? *Ecological Indicators*, 10: 734-743.

Guevara-Riba, A., Sahuquillo, A., Rubio, R., Rauret, G. (2004). Assessment of metal mobility in dredged harbour sediment from Barcelona, Spain. *Science of the Total Environment*, 321: 241-255.

Gupta, S., Singh, J. (2011). Evaluation of mollusc as sensitive indicator of heavy metal pollution in aquatic system: A review. *The IIOAB Journal*, 2 (1): 49-57.

Halpern, B., Walbridge, S., Selkoe, K., Kappel, C., Micheli, F., D'Agrosa, C., Bruno, J., Casey, K., Ebert, C., Fox, H., Fujita, R., Heinemann, D., Lenihan, H., Madin, E., Perry, M., Selig, E., Spalding, M., Steneck, R.

Watson, R. (2008). A global map of human impact on marine ecosystems. *Science*, 319: 948-952.

Hamza, W., Munawar, M. (2009). Protecting and managing the Arabian Gulf: past, present and future. *Aquatic Ecosystems Health and Management*, 12: 429-439.

Hashim, A., Hajjaj, M. (2005). Impact of desalination plants fluid effluents on integrity of seawater, with the Arabian Gulf in perspective, *Desalination*, 182: 373-393.

Hashim, M., Mukhopadhyay, S., Sahu, J., Sengupta, B. (2011). Remediation technologies for heavy metal contaminated groundwater. *Journal of Environmental Management*, 92: 2355-2388.

Hedge, L., Knott, A., Johnston, E. (2009). Dredging related metal bioaccumulation in oysters. *Marine Pollution Bulletin*, 58: 832-840.

Hoepner, T. (1999). A procedure for environmental impact assessment (EIA) for seawater desalination plants. *Desalination*, 124: 1-12.

Hogarth, P. (1999). *The biology of mangroves*. Oxford University Press, Oxford.

Hosono, T., Su, C., Siringan, F., Amano, A., Onodera, S. (2010). Effects of environmental regulation on heavy metal pollution decline in core sediments from Manila Bay. *Marine Pollution Bulletin*, 60: 780-785.

Hosono, T., Su, C., Delinom, R., Umezawa, Y., Toyota, T., Kaneko, S. Taniguchi, M. (2011). Decline in heavy metal contamination in marine sediments in Jakarta Bay, Indonesia due to increasing environmental regulations. *Estuarine, Coastal and Shelf Science*, 92: 297-306.

Hutchings, P. (1998). Biodiversity and functioning of polychaetes in benthic sediments. *Biodiversity and Conservation*, 7: 1133-1145.

Islam, M., Tanaka, M. (2004). Impacts of pollution on coastal and marine ecosystems including coastal and marine fisheries and approach for management: a review and synthesis. *Marine Pollution Bulletin*, 48: 624-649.

IAIA, International Association for Impact Assessment (1999). Principles of environmental impact assessment best practice. *IAIA and Institute for Environmental Assessment*, UK.

Jaber, J., Probert, S. (1999). Environmental impact assessment for the proposed oil-shale integrated tri-generation plant. *Applied Energy*, 62: 169-209.

Javed, M. (2006). Studies on metal contamination levels in plankton and their role as biological indicator of water pollution in the river Ravi. *Pakistan Journal of Biological Sciences*. 9: 313-317.

Joksimovic, D., Tomic, I., Stankovic, A., Jovic, M., Stankovic, S. (2011). Trace metal concentrations in Mediterranean blue mussel and surface sediments and evaluation of the mussels quality and possible risks of high human consumption. *Food Chemistry*, 127: 632-637.

Joydas, T., Qurban, M., Al-Suwailem, A., Krishnakumar, P., Nazeer, Z., Cali, N. (2012). Macrobenthic community structure in the northern Saudi waters of the Gulf, 14 years after the 1991 oil spill. *Marine Pollution Bulletin*, 64: 325-335.

Jones, D. Plaza, J., Watt, I., Al-Sanei, M. (1998). Long-term (1991-1995) monitoring of the intertidal biota of Saudi Arabia after 1991 Gulf War oil spill. *Marine Pollution Bulletin*, 36: 472-489.

Juma, H., Al-Madany, I. (2008). Concentration of heavy metals in the territorial seawater of the Kingdom of Bahrain, Arabian Gulf. *Arab Gulf Journal of Scientific Research*, 26: 19-32.

Kennish, M. (2001). *Practical handbook of marine science*. CRC Press, London.

Khalaf, A. and Redha, M. (2001). Rehabilitation of water production facilities of the Ministry of Electricity and Water, State of Bahrain. *Desalination*, 138: 319-328.

Khan, N. (2007). Multiple stressors and ecosystem-based management in the Gulf. *Aquatic Ecosystem Health Management*, 10: 259-267.

Khan, N. (2008). Integrated management of pollution stress in the Gulf. In Abuzinada, A., Barth, H., Krupp, F., Boer, B., Al Abdessalaam, T. (eds), *Protecting the Gulf's marine ecosystems from pollution*. Birthauser, Verlag/Switzerland, pp. 27-92.

Khan, N, Price, P. (2002). Legal and institutional frameworks, In: Khan, N., Munawar, M., Price, A. (eds). *The Gulf ecosystem: Health and sustainability*. Backhuys Publishers, Leiden.

Khan, N., Munawar, M., Price, A. (2002). *The Gulf ecosystem: Health and sustainability*. Backhuys Publishers, Leiden, pp. 399-424.

Kureishy, T. (1991). Heavy metals in algae around the coast of Qatar. *Marine Pollution Bulletin*, 22: 414-416.

Kureishy, T., Abdelmoati, M., Al-Muftah, A. (1995). Marine Algae as biondicators of pollution levels in the Arabian Gulf. *Qatar University Science Journal*, 15: 215-221.

Lattemann, S., Hoepner, T.,(2008a). Environmental impact and impact assessment of seawater desalination. *Desalination*, 220: 1-15.

Lattemann, S., Hopner, T. (2008b). Impacts of seawater desalination plants on the marine environment of the Gulf, in: A. Abuzinada, H. Barth, F. Krupp,

B. Boer, T. Abdessalaam (Eds.), *Protecting the Gulf's Marine Ecosystems from Pollution*, Birkhauser, 191-205 pp.

Lavoie, I., Vincent, W., Pienitz, R., Painchaud, J. (2004). Benthic algae as bionidicators of agricultural pollution in the streams and rivers of Southern Quebec (Canada). *Aquatic Ecosystem Health and Management*, 7 (1): 43-58.

Lee, D., Eom, K., Kim, G., Baeck, G. (2010). Scoping the effective marine environmental assessment of dredging and ocean disposal of coastal sediments in Korea. *Marine Policy*, 34: 1082-1092.

Literathy, P., Khan, N. Linden, O. (2002). Oil and petroleum industry. In: *The Gulf ecosystem: Health and Sustainability*, N. Khan, M. Munawar and A. Price (eds.). Backhuys Publishers, Leiden, pp. 127-156.

Lozano, G. Hardisson, A., Gutierez, A.J. and Lafuente, M.A. (2003). Lead and cadmium levels in coastal benthic algae (seaweeds) of Tenerife, Canary Islands. *Environmental International*, 28: 627-631

Madany, I., Wahab, A., Al-Alawi, Z. (1996). Trace metals concentrations in marine organisms from the coastal areas of Bahrain, Arabian Gulf. *Water, Air and Soil Pollution*, 91: 233-248.

Massoud, M., Al-Abdali, F., Al-Ghadban, A. (1998). The status of oil pollution in the Arabian Gulf by the end of 1993. *Environment International*, 24: 11-22.

MEMAC (Marine Emergency Mutual Aid Centre). (2003). *Oil spill incidents in ROPME Sea area* (1965-2002). MEMAC, Bahrain.

Miri, R. and Chouikhi, A. (2005). Ecotoxicological marine impacts from seawater desalination plants. *Desalination*, 182: 403-410.

Moberg, F., Folke, C. (1999). Ecological goods and services of coral reef ecosystems. *Ecological Economics*, 29: 215-233.

Moberg, F., Ronnback, P. (2003). Ecosystem services of tropical seascape: interactions, substitutions and restoration. *Ocean and Coastal Management*, 46: 27-46.

Mohamed, A. (2002). Trace metal concentrations in marine algae *Hormophysa triquetra*, Bahrain Coastline (Arabian Gulf). *Pollution Research*, 21 (4): 397-402.

Mohammed, S. (2003). Population parameters of the pearl oyster *Pinctada radiata* (Leach) in Qatari waters, Arabian Gulf. *Turkish Journal of Zoology*, 37: 339-343.

Mohamed, A., Maraqa, M., Al-Handhaly, J. (2005). Impact of land disposal of reject brine from desalination plants on soil and groundwater. *Desalination*, 182: 411-433.

Munawar, M., Price, A., Munawar, I., Carou, S., Niblock, H. and Lorimer, J. (2002). Aquatic ecosystem health of the Arabian Gulf: Status and research needs. In: *The Gulf ecosystem: Health and Sustainability*, N. Khan, M. Munawar and A. Price (eds.). Backhuys Publishers, Leiden, pp. 303-325.

Musaiger, A. and D'Souza, R. (2008). Chemical composition of raw fish consumed in Bahrain. *Pakistan Journal of Biological Sciences*, 11: 55-61.

Naik, M., Oandey, A., Dubey, S. (2012). Bioremediation of metals mediated by marine bacteria. In: T. Satyanarayana et al. (eds.), *Microorganisms in Environmental Management*, Springer, pp. 665-682.

Naser, H., Bythell, J., Thomason, J. (2008). Ecological assessment: an initial evaluation of ecological input in environmental impact assessment reports in Bahrain. *Impact Assessment and Project Appraisal*, 26 (3): 201-208.

Naser, H. (2010a). *Using macrobenthos as tool for ecological impact assessment: application in environmental impact assessment (EIA)*. Lambert Academic Publishing, Saarbrucken.

Naser, H. (2010b) Testing taxonomic resolution levels for detecting environmental impacts using macrobenthic assemblages in tropical waters. *Environmental Monitoring and Assessment*, 170: 435-444.

Naser, H. (2011a). Human impacts on marine biodiversity: macrobenthos in Bahrain, Arabian Gulf. In: *The importance of biological interactions in the study of Biodiversity*, J. Lopez-Pujol (ed.), InTech Publishing. Croatia, pp. 109-126.

Naser, H. (2011b). Effects of reclamation on macrobenthic assemblages in the coastline of the Arabian Gulf: A microcosm experimental approach. *Marine Pollution Bulletin*, 62: 520-524.

Naser, H. (2012a). Metal concentrations in marine sediments influenced by anthropogenic activities in Bahrain, Arabian Gulf. In: *Metal contaminations: sources, detection and environmental impacts,* Shao Hong-Bo (Editor), NOVA Science Publishers, Inc. New York, pp.157-175.

Naser, H. (2012b). Evaluation of the environmental impact assessment system in Bahrain. *Journal of Environmental Protection*, 3 (2): 233-239.

Nayar, S., Goh, B. and Chou, L. (2004). Environmental impact of heavy metals from dredged and resuspended sediments on phytoplankton and bacteria assessed in in situ mesocosms. *Ecotoxicology and Environmental Safety,* 59: 349-369.

Netzband, A., Adnitt, C. (2009). Dredging management practices for the environment: A structured selection approach 3. *Terra et Aqua*, 114: 3-8.

Newell, R. Seiderer, L., Hitchcock, D. (1998). The impact of dredging works in coastal waters: a review of the sensitivity to disturbance and subsequent recovery of biological resources on the sea bed. *Oceanography and Marine Biology: an Annual Review*, 36: 127-178.

Nobi, E., Dilipan, E., Thangaradjou, T., Sivakumar, K., Kannan, L. (2010). Geochemical and geo-statistical assessment of heavy metals concentration in the sediment of different coastal ecosystems of Andaman Island, India. *Estuarine, Coastal and Shelf Science*, 87: 253-264.

Noble, B. (2010). *Introduction to environmental impact assessment: a guide to principles and practices*. Oxford University Press, Oxford.

Nyamangara, J., Bangira, C., Taruvinga, T., Masona, Nyemba, A. and Ndlovu, D. (2008). Effects of sewage and industrial effluents on the concentration of Zn, Cu, Pb and Cd in water and sediments along waterfalls stream and lower Mukuvisi River in Harare, Zimbabwe. *Physics and Chemistry of the Earth*, 33: 708-713.

Osman, A., Kloas, W. (2010). Water quality and heavy monitoring in water, sediments, and tissues of the African catfish *Clarias gariepinus* (Burchell, 1722) from the River Nile, Egypt. *Journal of Environmental Protection*, 1: 389-400.

Perez-Lopez, M., Alonso, J., Novoa-Valinas, M., Melgar, M. (2003). Assessment of heavy metal contamination of seawater and marine limpet, *Patella vulgata* L., from Northwest Spain. *Journal of Environmental Science and Health*, 38 (12): 2845-2856.

Phillips, R., 2003. The seagrasses of the Arabian Gulf and Arabian Region. In: Green, E., Short, F. (Eds.), *World Atlas of Seagrasses*. UNEP-WCMC.

Picado, A., Bebianno, M., Costa, M., Ferreira, A., Vale, C. (2007). Biomarkers: a strategic tool in the assessment of environmental quality of coastal waters. *Hydrobiologia*, 587: 79-87.

Pourang, N., Nikouyan, A., Dennis, J. (2005). Trace element concentrations in fish, surficial sediments and water from northern part of the Persian Gulf. *Environmental Monitoring and Assessment*, 109: 293–316.

Preen, A. (2004). Distribution, abundance and conservation status of dugongs and dolphins in the southern and western Arabian Gulf. *Biological Conservation*, 118: 205- 218.

Preen, A., Das, H., Al-Rumaidh, M., Hodgson, A. (2012). Dugongs in Arabia; In: E. Himes, J. Reynolds III, L. Aragones, A. Mignucci-Giannoni, M. Marmontel (Eds.) *Sirenian conservation: Issues and strategies in developing countries*. University Press of Florida, Gainesville.

Price, A., Robinson, J., (1993.) The 1991 Gulf War: Coastal and marine environmental consequences. *Marine Pollution Bulletin*, 27, pp. 380.

Price, A., Sheppard, C. (1991). The Gulf: past, present and possible future states. *Marine Pollution Bulletin* 22 (5): 222-227.

Price, A., Sheppard, C., Roberts, C. (1993). The Gulf: Its biological setting. *Marine Pollution Bulletin*, 27: 9-15.

Rahman, M., Ishiga, H. (2012). Trance metal concentrations in tidal flat coastal sediments, Yamaguchi Prefecture, southwest Japan. *Environmental Monitoring and Assessment*, 184: 5755-5771.

Rappe, R. (2010). Population and community level indicator in assessment of heavy metal contamination in seagrass ecosystem. *Coastal Marine Science*, 34: 198-204.

Riegl, B, Purkis, S. (2012). *Coral reefs of the Gulf: adaptation to climatic extremes.* Springer, Dordrecht Heidelberg.

Reis, P., Salgado, M., Vasconcelos, A. (2012). *Chthamalus montagui* as biomonitor of metal contamination in the northwest coast of Portugal. *Environmental Monitoring and Assessment*, 184: 5421-5437.

ROPME. Regional Organization for the Protection of the Marine Environment (2003). State of the marine environment report. Regional Organization for the Protection of the Marine Environment (ROPME), Kuwait.

ROPME, Regional Organization for the Protection of the Marine Environment (2005a). *Guidelines for management of industrial wastewater for the ROPME region.* Kuwait.

ROPME, Regional Organization for the Protection of the Marine Environment (2005b). *Guidelines on sewage treatment and disposal for the ROPME region, including guidance for submarine outfall structures.* Kuwait.

Ruilian, Y., Xing, Y., Yuanhui, Z., Gongren, H., Xianglin, T. (2008). Heavy metal pollution in intertidal sediments from Quanzhou Bay, China. *Journal of Environmental Sciences*, 20: 664-669.

Ryu, J., Khim, J., Kang, S., Kang, D., Lee, C., Koh, C. (2011). The impact of heavy metal pollution gradients in sediment on benthic macrofauna at population and community levels. *Environmental Pollution*, 159: 2622-2629.

Sadiq, M. (2002). Metal contamination in sediments from a desalination plant effluent outfall area. *The Science of the Total Environment*, 287: 37-44.

Saenger, P. (2002). *Mangrove Ecology, Silviculture and Conservation.* Kluwer Academic Publishers, London.

Salas, F., Marcos, C., Neto, J., Patricio, J., Perez-Ruzafa, A., Marques, J. (2006). User-friendly guide for using benthic ecological indicators in coastal and marine quality assessment. *Ocean and Coastal Management,* 49: 308–331.

Sale, P., Feary, D., Burt, J., Bauman, A., Cavalcante, G., Drouillard, K., Kjerfve, B., Marquis, E., Trick, C., Usseglio, P., Van Lavieren, H. (2010). The growing need for sustainable ecological management of marine communities of the Persian Gulf. *Ambio,* 40: 4-17.

Sdiri, A., Higashi, T., Jamoussi, F., Bouaziz, S. (2012). Effects of impurities on the removal of heavy metals by natural limestones in aqueous systems. *Journal of Environmental Management,* 93: 245-253.

Shatti, J., Abdullah, T. (1999). Marine pollution due to wastewater discharge in Kuwait. *Water Science and Technology,* 40 (7): 33-39.

Sheppard, C., Price, A. and Roberts, C. (1992). Marine ecology of the Arabian Region: *Patterns and processes in extreme tropical environments.* Academic Press, London.

Sheppard, C., Al-Husiani, M., Al-Jamali, F., Al-Yamani, F., Baldwin, R., Bishop, J., Benzoni, F., Dutrieux, E., Dulvy, N., Durvasula, S., Jones, D., Loughland, R., Medio, D., Nithyanandan, M., Pilling, G., Polikarpov, I., Price, A., Purkis, S., Riegl, B., Saburova, M., Namin, K., Taylor, O., Wilson, S., Zainal, K. (2010). The Gulf: A young sea in decline. *Marine Pollution Bulletin,* 60: 3-38.

Shriadah, M. (1998). Metal pollution in marine sediments of the United Arab Emirates creeks along the Arabian Gulf shoreline. *Bulletin of Environmental Contamination and Toxicology,* 60: 417-424.

Shriadah, M. (1999). Heavy metals in mangrove sediments of the United Arab Emirates shoreline (Arabian Gulf). *Water, Air and Soil Pollution,* 166: 523-534.

Singh, K., Mohan, D., Sinha, S., Dalwani, R. (2004). Impact assessment of treated/untreated wastewater toxicants discharged by sewage treatment plants on health, agricultural, and environmental quality in wastewater disposal area. *Chemosphere,* 55: 227-255.

Singh, S., Tack, F., Verloo, M. (1998). Land disposal of heavy metal contaminated dredged sediments: a review of environmental aspects. *Land Contamination and Reclamation,* 6: 149-158.

Smith, R., Purnama, A.,. Al-Barwani, H. (2007). Sensitivity of hypersaline Arabian Gulf to Seawater desalination plants, *Applied Mathematical Modelling,* 31 2347-2354.

Smith, S., Rule, M. (2001). The effects of dredge-spoil dumping on a shallow water soft sediment community in the Solitary Island Marine Park, NSW, Australia. *Marine Pollution Bulletin,* 42: 1040-1048.

Snelgrove, P. (1998). The biodiversity of macrofaunal organism in marine sediments. *Biodiversity and Conservation*, 7: 1123-1132.

Soltmann, U., Matys, S., Kieszig. G., Pompe, W., Bottcher, H. (2010). Algae-silica hybrid materials for biosorption of heavy metals. *Journal of Water resource and Protection*, 3: 115-122.

Tack, F., Singh, S. and Verloo, M. (1998). Heavy metal concentrations in consecutive saturation extracts of dredged sediment derived surface soils. *Environmental Pollution*, 103: 109-115.

Tarique, Q., Burger, J., Reinfelder, J. (2012). Metal concentrations in organs of clam *Amiantis umbonella* and their use in monitoring metal contamination of coastal sediments. *Water, Air and Soil Pollution*, 223: 2125-2136.

Thangaradjou, T., Nobi, E., Dilipan, E., Sivakumar, K., Susila, S. (2010). Heavy metal enrichment in seagrasses of Andaman Islands and its implication to the health of the coastal ecosystem. *Indian Journal of Marine Sciences*, 39: 85-91.

Thangaradjou, T., Raja, S., Subhashini, P., Nobi, E., Dilipan, E. (2013). Heavy metal enrichment in the seagrasses of Lakshadweep group islands-A multivariate statistical analysis. *Environmental Monitoring and Assessment*, 185: 673-685.

Topcuoglo, S., Guven, K.C., Balkis, N. and Kirbasoglu, C. (2003). Heavy Metal monitoring of marine algae from the Turkish coast of the Black Sea, 1998-2000. *Chemosphere*, 52: 1683-1688

Torres, M., Barros, M., Campos, S., Pinto, E., Rajamani, S., Savre, R., Colepicolo, P. (2008). Biochemical biomarkers in algae and marine pollution: A review. *Ecotoxicology and Environmental Safety*, 71: 1-5.

Treweek, J. (1999). *Ecological Impact Assessment*. Blackwell Science Ltd, Oxford.

Tsiourtis, N. (2008). Criteria and procedure for selecting a site for a desalination plant. *Desalination*, 221: 114-125.

Uddin, S., Gevao, B., Al-Ghadban, A., Nithyanandan, Al-Shamroukh, D. (2012). Acidification in the Arabian Gulf – Insights from pH and temperature measurements. *Journal of Environmental Monitoring*, 14:1479-1482.

UNEP (2008). *Desalination resource and guidance manual for environmental impacts assessment*. United Nations Environmental Programme, Regional Offices of West Asia, Manama, and World Health Organization, Regional Office for the Eastern Mediterranean, Cairo.

Valdes, J. (2012). Heavy metal distribution and enrichment in sediments of Mejillones Bay (23° S), Chile: a spatial and temporal approach. *Environmental Monitoring and Assessment*, 184: 5283-5294.

Van Lavieren, H., Burt, J., Feary, D., Cavalcante, G., Marquis, E., Benedetti, L., Trick, C., Kjerfve, B., Sale, P. (2011). Managing the growing impacts of development on fragile coastal and marine ecosystems: lessons from the Gulf. *A policy report, UNU-INWEH*, Hamilton, ON, Canada.

Wake, H. (2005). Oil refineries: a review of their ecological impacts on the aquatic environment. *Estuarine, Coastal and Shelf Science*, 62: 131-140.

Williams, C., 1996. Combating marine pollution from land-based activities: Australian initiatives. *Ocean and Coastal Management*, 33: 87–112.

Zhou, Q., Zhang, J., Fu, J., Shi, J. Jiang, G. (2008). Biomonitoring: an appealing tool for assessment of metal pollution in the aquatic ecosystem. *Analytic Chimica Acta*, 606: 135-150.

Zyadah, M., Almoteiry, M. (2012). Evaluation of environmental pollution in the Arabian Gulf coast of the Eastern Province, SA. *Asian Transactions on Basic and Applied Sciences*, 2 (3): 14-21.

INDEX